Fairy & Folk Tales from Around the World

Fairy & Folk Tales from Around the World

SIRIUS

SIRIUS

This edition published in 2019 by Sirius Publishing, a division of Arcturus Publishing Limited,
26/27 Bickels Yard, 151–153 Bermondsey Street,
London SE1 3HA

Copyright © Arcturus Holdings Limited

All rights reserved. No part of this publication may be reproduced, stored in a retrieval system, or transmitted, in any form or by any means, electronic, mechanical, photocopying, recording or otherwise, without prior written permission in accordance with the provisions of the Copyright Act 1956 (as amended). Any person or persons who do any unauthorised act in relation to this publication may be liable to criminal prosecution and civil claims for damages.

ISBN: 978-1-78950-400-2
AD007190UK

Printed in China

CONTENTS

Introduction............................. 7

The Bamboo-cutter and the Moon-child
(Japanese)............................. 9

The Wonderful Pear-Tree (Chinese) 27

Mangita and Larina (Filipino) 30

Makota Radja-Radja (Malay)................ 33

Beereeun the Mirage Maker (Australian) 74

How the Tiger Got His Stripes (Vietnamese) ... 83

The Valiant Chattee-maker (Indian)........... 89

The Golden Mountain (Russian) 97

The Crow Peri (Persian).................. 102

The Betrothed of Destiny (Armenian)........ 118

The Palace of Eagles (Jewish).............. 123

Fortunatus and His Purse (Cypriot).......... 131

The Speaking Grapes, the Smiling Apple
and the Tinkling Apricot (Magyar)........ 139

The Good Ferryman Captures the Mermaid
    (Polish) 142

Signor Lattanzio (Italian) 154

The Three Oranges (Italian) 157

Felicia and the Pot of Pinks (French) 162

The Dwarfie Stone (Scottish) 172

The Legend of Knockgrafton (Irish) 186

The Hedgehog, the Jackal and the Lion
    (Moorish) 193

The False Prince and the True (Portuguese) . . . 198

Crocodile's Treason (South African) 207

Elephant and Tortoise (Namibian) 213

Thunder and Anansi (West African) 215

How the Brazilian Beetles Got Their
    Gorgeous Coats (Brazilian) 219

Pauppukkeewis (Native American) 223

Battle of the Owls (Hawaiian) 238

INTRODUCTION

The stories and tales in this collection come from all over the world, with Japan, Brazil, Hawaii, Australia and Scotland, to name but a few, represented.

Many fairy and folk tales find their origins in the oral tradition. Oral storytelling is believed to have existed for almost as long as humans themselves. In one of the oldest known cultures, that of the Australian Aborigines, storytelling played a vital role. A tale from this tradition, 'Beereeun the Mirage Maker', is inlcuded. A storyteller would often wander from town to town, even country to country, sharing their stories, gathering and exchanging them with other tellers. As these storytellers travelled, so too did their tales, evolving as they went. Each teller, of course, added their own personality in the telling, along with the traditions of their homeland, taking in their experiences, the trends of the day and developing the stories to reflect what was popular or newsworthy at the time.

It was in this way that the tales of nations far and wide developed and grew. These stories and their tellers were highly sought after and considered of great import, as such they were expected to know all the new tales of the day. It was the importance of these tales, their bringing together of peoples to hear the telling and their recording of a shared history that eventually saw them collected and written down. The written tales, as the oral ones before them, also took on the ideas and tastes of their authors. It is this rich history and tradition of storytelling that has resulted in the stories of one nation reflecting those of many others, both near and far.

In this collection you will find samples of this deep and wonderful tradition from more than 25 countries. Within them you may spot tales similar to those that you already know, or you may find a tale that is new to you entirely. These tales offer a fascinating glimpse into not only their country of origin but into the world as a whole.

Though many of the earliest collectors of such tales, like Jacob and Wilhelm Grimm, believed them to be important for the preservation of the history of their specific nation, it has often become difficult to discover in which nation a story truly originated. One example here, 'The Three Oranges', is the earliest known written version of the tale and comes from Italy, but there are also versions from Norway and Spain and perhaps even further afield. The traditional tales of many countries are representeted from Vietnam to Russian and from China to Armenia. Enjoy this fascinating collection of stories filled with colourful creatures and characters as they take you around the world.

THE BAMBOO-CUTTER
AND THE MOON-CHILD

(JAPANESE)

Long, long ago, there lived an old bamboo wood-cutter. He was very poor and sad, for Heaven had no child sent to cheer his old age, and in his heart, there was no hope of rest from work till he died and was laid in the quiet grave. Every morning he went forth into the woods and hills wherever the bamboo reared its lithe green plumes against the sky. When he had made his choice, he would cut down these feathers of the forest and split them lengthwise or cut them into joints, and he would carry the bamboo wood home. He would make it into various articles for the household, and he and his old wife gained a small livelihood by selling them.

One morning as usual, he had gone out to his work, and having found a nice clump of bamboos, had set to work to cut some of them down. Suddenly the green grove of bamboos was flooded with a bright soft light, as if the full moon had risen over the spot. Looking around in astonishment, he saw that the brilliance was streaming from one bamboo. The old man, full of wonder, dropped his axe and went towards the light. On nearer approach he saw that this soft splendour came from a hollow in the green bamboo stem, and still more wonderful to behold, in the midst of the brilliance stood a tiny human being, only three inches in height and exquisitely beautiful in appearance.

'You must be sent to be my child, for I find you here among the bamboos where lies my daily work,' said the old man, and taking the little creature in his hand he took it home to his wife to bring up. The tiny girl was so exceedingly beautiful and so small that the old woman put her into a basket to safeguard her from the least possibility of being hurt in any way.

The old couple were now very happy, for it had been a lifelong regret that they had no children of their own, and with joy, they now expended all the love of their old age on the little child who had come to them in so marvellous a manner.

From this time on, the old man often found gold in the notches of the bamboos when he hewed them down and cut them up; not only gold, but precious stones also, so that by degrees he became rich. He built himself a fine house and was no longer known as the poor bamboo woodcutter but as a wealthy man.

Three months passed quickly, and in that time the bamboo child had, wonderful to say, become a full-grown girl, so her foster-parents did up her hair and dressed her in beautiful kimonos. She was of such wondrous beauty that they placed her behind the screens like a princess and allowed no one to see her, waiting upon her themselves. It seemed as if she were made of light, for the house was filled with a soft shining, so that even in the dark of night it was like daytime. Her presence seemed to have a benign influence on those there. Whenever the old man felt sad, he had only to look upon his foster-daughter and his sorrow vanished, and he became as happy as when he was a youth.

At last the day came for the naming of their new-found child, so the old couple called in a celebrated name-giver, and he gave her the name of Princess Moonlight because her body gave forth so much soft bright light that she might have been a daughter of the Moon God.

For three days the festival was kept up with song and dance and music. All the friends and relations of the old couple were present, and great was their enjoyment of the festivities held to celebrate the naming of Princess Moonlight. Everyone who saw her declared that there never had been seen anyone so lovely. All the beauties throughout the length and breadth of the land would grow pale beside her, so they said. The fame of the Princess's loveliness spread far and wide, and many were the suitors who desired to win her hand or even so much as to see her.

Suitors from far and near posted themselves outside the house, and made little holes in the fence, in the hope of catching a glimpse of the Princess as she went from one room to the other along the veranda. They stayed there day and night, sacrificing even their sleep for a chance of seeing her, but all in vain. Then they approached the house, and tried to speak to the old man and his wife or some of the servants, but not even this was granted them.

Still, in spite of all this disappointment they stayed on day after day, and night after night, and counted it as nothing, so great was their desire to see the Princess.

At last, however, most of the men, seeing how hopeless their quest was, lost heart and hope both, and returned to their homes. All except five Knights, whose ardour and determination, instead of waning, seemed to wax greater with obstacles. These five men even went without their meals, and took snatches of whatever they could get brought to them, so that they might always stand outside the dwelling. They stood there in all weathers, in sunshine and in rain.

Sometimes they wrote letters to the Princess, but no answer was vouchsafed to them. Then when letters failed to draw any reply, they wrote poems to her telling her of the hopeless love which kept them from sleep, from food, from rest, and even from their homes. Still Princess Moonlight gave no sign of having received their verses.

In this hopeless state the winter passed. The snow and frost and the cold winds gradually gave place to the gentle warmth of spring. Then the summer came, and the sun burned white and scorching in the heavens above and on the earth beneath, and still these faithful Knights kept watch and waited. At the end of these long months they called out to the old bamboo-cutter and entreated him to have some mercy upon them and to show them the Princess, but he answered only that as he was not her real father he could not insist on her obeying him against her wishes.

The five Knights on receiving this stern answer returned to their several homes, and pondered over the best means of touching the proud Princess's heart, even so much as to grant them a hearing. They took their rosaries in hand, knelt before their household shrines, burned precious incense, and prayed to Buddha to give them their heart's desire. Thus several days passed, but even so they could not rest in their homes.

So again they set out for the bamboo-cutter's house. This time the old man came out to see them, and they asked him to let them know if it was the Princess's resolution never to see any man whatsoever, and they implored him to speak for them and to tell her the greatness of their love, and how long they had waited through the cold of winter and the heat of summer, sleepless and roofless through all weathers, without food and without rest, in the ardent hope of winning her, and they were willing to consider this long vigil as pleasure if she would but give them one chance of pleading their cause with her.

The old man lent a willing ear to their tale of love, for in his inmost heart he felt sorry for these faithful suitors and would have liked to see his lovely foster-daughter married to one of them. So he went in to Princess Moonlight and said reverently:

'Although you have always seemed to me to be a heavenly being, yet I have had the trouble of bringing you up as my own child and you have been glad of the protection of my roof. Will you refuse to do as I wish?'

Then Princess Moonlight replied that there was nothing she would not do for him, that she honoured and loved him as her own father, and that as for herself she could not remember the time before she came to earth.

The old man listened with great joy as she spoke these dutiful words. Then he told her how anxious he was to see her safely and happily married before he died.

'I am an old man, over 70 years of age, and my end may come any time now. It is necessary and right that you should see these five suitors and choose one of them.'

'Oh, why,' said the Princess in distress, 'must I do this? I have no wish to marry now.'

'I found you,' answered the old man, 'many years ago, when you were a little creature three inches high, in the midst of a great white light. The light streamed from the bamboo in which you were hid and led me to you. So I have always thought that you were more than mortal woman. While I am alive it is right for you to remain as you are if you wish to do so, but someday I shall cease to be and who will take care of you then? Therefore I pray you to meet these five brave men one at a time and make up your mind to marry one of them!'

Then the Princess answered that she felt sure that she was not as beautiful as perhaps report made her out to be, and that even if she consented to marry any one of them, not really knowing her before, his heart might change afterwards. So as she did not feel sure of them, even though her father told her they were worthy Knights, she did not feel it wise to see them.

'All you say is very reasonable,' said the old man, 'but what kind of men will you consent to see? I do not call these five men who have waited on you for months, light-hearted. They have stood outside this house through the winter and the summer, often denying themselves food and sleep so that they may win you. What more can you demand?'

Then Princess Moonlight said she must make further trial of their love before she would grant their request to interview her. The five warriors were to prove their love by each bringing her from distant countries something that she desired to possess.

That same evening the suitors arrived and began to play their flutes in turn and to sing their self-composed songs telling of their great and tireless love. The bamboo-cutter went out to them and offered them his sympathy for all they had endured and all the patience they had shown in their desire to win his foster-daughter. Then he gave them her message, that she would consent to marry whosoever was successful in bringing her what she wanted. This was to test them.

The five all accepted the trial, and thought it an excellent plan, for it would prevent jealousy between them.

Princess Moonlight then sent word to the First Knight that she requested him to bring her the stone bowl which had belonged to Buddha in India.

The Second Knight was asked to go to the Mountain of Horai, said to be situated in the Eastern Sea, and to bring her a branch of the wonderful tree that grew on its summit. The roots of this tree were of silver, the trunk of gold, and the branches bore as fruit white jewels.

The Third Knight was told to go to China and search for the fire-rat and to bring her its skin.

The Fourth Knight was told to search for the dragon that carried on its head the stone radiating five colours and to bring the stone to her.

The Fifth Knight was to find the swallow which carried a shell in its stomach and to bring the shell to her.

The old man thought these very hard tasks and hesitated to carry the messages, but the Princess would make no other conditions. So her commands were issued word for word to the five men who, when they heard what was required of them, were all disheartened and disgusted at what seemed to them the impossibility of the tasks given them and returned to their own homes in despair.

But after a time, when they thought of the Princess, the love in their hearts revived for her, and they resolved to make an attempt to get what she desired of them.

The First Knight sent word to the Princess that he was starting out that day on the quest of Buddha's bowl, and he hoped soon to bring it to her. But he had not the courage to go all the way to India, for in those days travelling was very difficult and full of danger, so he went to one of the temples in Kyoto and took a stone bowl from the altar there, paying the priest a large sum of money for it. He then wrapped it in a cloth of gold and waited quietly for three years before he returned and carried it to the old man.

Princess Moonlight wondered that the Knight should have returned so soon. She took the bowl from its gold wrapping, expecting it to make the room full of light, but it did not shine at all, so she knew that it was a sham thing and not the true bowl of Buddha. She returned it at once and refused to see him. The Knight threw the bowl away and returned to his home in despair. He gave up now all hopes of ever winning the Princess.

The Second Knight told his parents that he needed a change of air for his health, for he was ashamed to tell them that love for the Princess Moonlight was the real cause of his leaving them. He then left his home, at the same time sending word to the Princess that he was setting out for Mount Horai in the hope of getting her a branch of the gold and silver tree which she so much wished to have. He only allowed his servants to accompany him halfway, and then sent them back. He reached the seashore and embarked on a small ship, and after sailing away for three days he landed and employed several carpenters to build him a house contrived in such a way that no one could get access to it. He then shut himself up with six skilled jewellers, and endeavoured to make such a gold and silver branch as he thought would satisfy the Princess as having come from the wonderful tree growing on Mount Horai. Everyone whom he had asked declared that Mount Horai belonged to the land of fable and not to fact.

When the branch was finished, he took his journey home and tried to make himself look as if he were wearied and worn out

THE BAMBOO-CUTTER AND THE MOON-CHILD 17

with travel. He put the jewelled branch into a lacquer box and carried it to the bamboo-cutter, begging him to present it to the Princess.

The old man was quite deceived by the travel-stained appearance of the Knight, and thought that he had only just returned from his long journey with the branch. So he tried to persuade the Princess to consent to see the man. But she remained silent and looked very sad. The old man began to take out the branch and praised it as a wonderful treasure to be found nowhere in the whole land. Then he spoke of the Knight, how handsome and how brave he was to have undertaken a journey to so remote a place as the Mount of Horai.

Princess Moonlight took the branch in her hand and looked at it carefully. She then told her foster-parent that she knew it was impossible for the man to have obtained a branch from the gold and silver tree growing on Mount Horai so quickly or so easily, and she was sorry to say she believed it artificial.

The old man then went out to the expectant Knight, who had now approached the house, and asked where he had found the branch. Then the man did not scruple to make up a long story.

'Two years ago I took a ship and started in search of Mount Horai. After going before the wind for some time I reached the far Eastern Sea. Then a great storm arose and I was tossed about for many days, losing all count of the points of the compass, and finally we were blown ashore on an unknown island. Here I found the place inhabited by demons who at one time threatened to kill and eat me. However, I managed to make friends with these horrible creatures. They helped me and my sailors to repair the boat, and I set sail again. Our food gave out, arid, we suffered much from sickness on board. At last, on the 500th day from the day of starting, I saw far off on the horizon what looked like the peak of a mountain. On nearer approach, this proved to be an island in the centre of which rose a high mountain. I landed, and after wandering about for two or three days, I saw a shining being coming towards me on the beach, holding in his hands a golden bowl. I went up to him and asked him if I had, by good chance, found the island of Mount Horai, and he answered:

'Yes, this is Mount Horai!'

'With much difficulty I climbed to the summit, where stood the golden tree growing with silver roots in the ground. The wonders of that strange land are many, and if I began to tell you about them I could never stop. In spite of my wish to stay there long, on breaking off the branch I hurried back. With utmost speed it has taken me 400 days to get back, and, as you see, my clothes are still damp from exposure on the long sea voyage. I have not even waited to change my raiment, so anxious was I to bring the branch to the Princess quickly.'

Just at this moment the six jewellers, who had been employed on the making of the branch, but not yet paid by the Knight, arrived at the house and sent in a petition to the Princess to be paid for their labour. They said that they had worked for over a 1,000 days making the branch of gold with its silver twigs and its jewelled fruit that was now presented to her by the Knight, but as yet they had received nothing in payment. So this Knight's deception was thus found out, and the Princess, glad of an escape from one more importunate suitor, was only too pleased to send back the branch. She called in the workmen and had them paid liberally, and they went away happy. But on the way home they were overtaken by the disappointed man, who beat them till they were nearly dead, for letting out the secret, and they barely escaped with their lives. The Knight then returned home, raging in his heart and in despair of ever winning the Princess, gave up society and retired to a solitary life among the mountains.

Now the Third Knight had a friend in China, so he wrote to him to get the skin of the fire-rat.

The virtue of any part of this animal was that no fire could harm it. He promised his friend any amount of money he liked to ask if only he could get him the desired article. As soon as the news came that the ship on which his friend had sailed home had come into port, he rode seven days on horseback to meet him. He handed his friend a large sum of money, and received the fire-rat's skin. When he reached home he put it carefully in a box and sent it in to the Princess while he waited outside for her answer.

The bamboo-cutter took the box from the Knight and, as usual, carried it in to her and tried to coax her to see the Knight at once, but Princess Moonlight refused, saying that she must first put the skin to the test by putting it into the fire. If it were the real thing it would not burn. So she took off the crêpe wrapper and opened the box, and then threw the skin into the fire. The skin crackled and burnt up at once, and the Princess knew that this man also had not fulfilled his word. So the Third Knight failed also.

Now the Fourth Knight was no more enterprising than the rest. Instead of starting out on the quest of the dragon bearing on its head the five-colour-radiating jewel, he called all his servants together and gave them the order to seek for it far and wide in Japan and China, and he strictly forbade any of them to return till they had found it.

His numerous retainers and servants started out in different directions with no intention of obeying what they considered an impossible order. They simply took a holiday, went to pleasant country places together, and grumbled at their master's unreasonableness.

The Knight meanwhile, thinking that his retainers could not fail to find the jewel, repaired to his house, and fitted it up beautifully for the reception of the Princess, he felt so sure of winning her.

One year passed away in weary waiting, and still his men did not return with the dragon-jewel. The Knight became desperate. He could wait no longer, so taking with him only two men he hired a ship and commanded the captain to go in search of the dragon. The captain and the sailors refused to undertake what they said was an absurd search, but the Knight compelled them at last to put out to sea.

When they had been a few days out they encountered a great storm which lasted so long that, by the time its fury abated, the Knight had determined to give up the hunt of the dragon. They were at last blown on shore, for navigation was primitive in those days. Worn out with his travels and anxiety, the fourth suitor gave himself up to rest. He had caught a very heavy cold, and had to go to bed with a swollen face.

The governor of the place, hearing of his plight, sent messengers with a letter inviting him to his house. While he was there thinking over all his troubles, his love for the Princess turned to anger, and he blamed her for all the hardships he had undergone. He thought that it was quite probable she had wished to kill him so that she might be rid of him, and in order to carry out her wish had sent him upon his impossible quest.

THE BAMBOO-CUTTER AND THE MOON-CHILD

At this point all the servants he had sent out to find the jewel came to see him, and were surprised to find praise instead of displeasure awaiting them. Their master told them that he was heartily sick of adventure, and said that he never intended to go near the Princess's house again in the future.

Like all the rest, the Fifth Knight failed in his quest – he could not find the swallow's shell.

By this time the fame of Princess Moonlight's beauty had reached the ears of the Emperor, and he sent one of the Court ladies to see if she were really as lovely as report said; if so he would summon her to the Palace and make her one of the ladies-in-waiting.

When the Court lady arrived, in spite of her father's entreaties, Princess Moonlight refused to see her. The Imperial messenger insisted, saying it was the Emperor's order. Then Princess Moonlight told the old man that if she was forced to go to the Palace in obedience to the Emperor's order, she would vanish from the earth.

When the Emperor was told of her persistence in refusing to obey his summons, and that if pressed to obey she would disappear altogether from sight, he determined to go and see her. So he planned to go on a hunting excursion in the neighbourhood of the bamboo-cutter's house and see the Princess himself. He sent word to the old man of his intention, and he received consent to the scheme. The next day the Emperor set out with his retinue, which he soon managed to outride. He found the bamboo-cutter's house and dismounted. He then entered the house and went straight to where the Princess was sitting with her attendant maidens.

Never had he seen anyone so wonderfully beautiful, and he could not but look at her, for she was more lovely than any human being as she shone in her own soft radiance. When Princess Moonlight became aware that a stranger was looking at her she tried to escape from the room, but the Emperor caught her and begged her to listen to what he had to say. Her only answer was to hide her face in her sleeves.

The Emperor fell deeply in love with her, and begged her to come to the Court, where he would give her a position of honour and everything she could wish for. He was about to send for one of the Imperial palanquins to take her back with him at once, saying that her grace and beauty should adorn a Court, and not be hidden in a bamboo-cutter's cottage.

But the Princess stopped him. She said that if she were forced to go to the Palace she would turn at once into a shadow, and even as she spoke she began to lose her form. Her figure faded from his sight while he looked.

The Emperor then promised to leave her free if only she would resume her former shape, which she did.

It was now time for him to return, for his retinue would be wondering what had happened to their Royal master when they missed him for so long. So he bade her good-bye, and left the house with a sad heart. Princess Moonlight was for him the most beautiful woman in the world. All others were dark beside her, and he thought of her night and day. His Majesty now spent much of his time in writing poems, telling her of his love and devotion, and sent them to her, and though she refused to see him again she answered with many verses of her own composing, which told him gently and kindly that she could never marry anyone on this earth. These little songs always gave him pleasure.

At this time her foster-parents noticed that night after night the Princess would sit on her balcony and gaze for hours at the moon, in a spirit of the deepest dejection, ending always in a burst of tears. One night the old man found her thus weeping as if her heart were broken, and he besought her to tell him the reason of her sorrow.

With many tears she told him that he had guessed rightly when he supposed her not to belong to this world, that she had in truth come from the moon, and that her time on earth would soon be over. On the 15th day of that very month of August her friends from the moon would come to fetch her, and she would have to return. Her parents were both there, but having spent a lifetime on the earth she had forgotten them, and also the moon-world to which she belonged. It made her weep, she said, to think of leaving her kind foster-parents, and the home where she had been happy for so long.

When her attendants heard this they were very sad, and could not eat or drink for sadness at the thought that the Princess was so soon to leave them.

The Emperor, as soon as the news was carried to him, sent messengers to the house to find out if the report were true or not.

The old bamboo-cutter went out to meet the Imperial messengers. The last few days of sorrow had told upon the old man; he had aged greatly, and looked much more than his 70 years. Weeping bitterly, he told them that the report was only too true, but he intended, however, to make prisoners of the envoys from the moon, and to do all he could to prevent the Princess from being carried back.

The men returned and told His Majesty all that had passed. On the 15th day of that month the Emperor sent a guard of 2,000 warriors to watch the house. One thousand stationed themselves on the roof, another thousand kept watch around all the entrances of the house. All around were trained archers with bows and arrows. The bamboo-cutter and his wife hid Princess Moonlight in an inner room.

The old man gave orders that no one was to sleep that night, all in the house were to keep a strict watch, and be ready to protect the Princess. With these precautions, and the help of the Emperor's men-at-arms, he hoped to withstand the moon-messengers, but the Princess told him that all these measures to keep her would be useless. When her people came for her nothing whatever could prevent them from carrying out their purpose. Even the Emperor's men would be powerless. Then she added with tears that she was very, very sorry to leave him and his wife, whom she had learned to love as her parents; that if she could do as she liked she would stay with them in their old age, and try to make some return for all the love and kindness they had showered upon her during all her earthly life.

The night wore on! The yellow harvest moon rose high in the heavens, flooding the world asleep with her golden light. Silence reigned over the pine and the bamboo forests, and on the roof where the thousand men-at-arms waited.

Then the night grew grey towards the dawn and all hoped that the danger was over and that Princess Moonlight would not have to leave them after all. Then suddenly the watchers saw a cloud form round the moon and while they looked this cloud began to roll earthwards. Nearer and nearer it came, and everyone saw with dismay that its course lay towards the house.

In a short time the sky was entirely obscured, till at last the cloud lay over the dwelling only ten feet off the ground. In the midst of the cloud there stood a flying chariot, and in the chariot a band of luminous beings. One amongst them, who looked like a king, appeared to be the chief. He stepped out of the chariot, and, poised in the air, called to the old man to come out.

'The time has come,' he said, 'for Princess Moonlight to return to the moon from where she came. She committed a grave fault, and as a punishment was sent to live down here for a time. We know what good care you have taken of the Princess, and we have rewarded you for this and have sent you wealth and prosperity. We put the gold in the bamboos for you to find.'

'I have brought up this Princess for 20 years and never once has she done a wrong thing, therefore the lady you are seeking cannot be this one,' said the old man. 'I pray you to look elsewhere.'

Then the messenger called aloud, saying:

'Princess Moonlight, come out from this lowly dwelling. Rest not here another moment.'

At these words the screens of the Princess's room slid open of their own accord, revealing the Princess shining in her own radiance, bright, wonderful, and full of beauty.

The messenger led her forth and placed her in the chariot. She looked back, and saw with pity the deep sorrow of the old man. She spoke to him many comforting words, and told him that it was not her will to leave him and that he must always think of her when looking at the moon.

The bamboo-cutter implored to be allowed to accompany her, but this was not permitted. The Princess took off her embroidered outer garment and gave it to him as a keepsake.

One of the moon beings in the chariot held a wonderful coat of wings, another had a vial full of the Elixir of Life which was given to the Princess to drink. She swallowed a little and was about to give the rest to the old man, but she was prevented from doing so.

The robe of wings was about to be put upon her shoulders, but she said:

'Wait a little. I must not forget my good friend the Emperor. I must write to him once more to say good-bye while still in this human form.'

In spite of the impatience of the messengers and charioteers, she kept them waiting while she wrote. She placed the vial of the Elixir of Life with the letter and gave them to the old man. She asked him to deliver them to the Emperor.

Then the chariot began to roll heavenwards towards the moon, and as they all gazed with tearful eyes at the receding Princess, the dawn broke, and in the rosy light of day the moonlight and all of them were lost amongst the fleecy clouds that were now wafted across the sky on the wings of the morning wind.

Princess Moonlight's letter was carried to the Palace. His Majesty was afraid to touch the Elixir of Life, so he sent it with the letter to the top of the most sacred mountain in the land, Mount Fuji, and there the Royal emissaries burnt it on the summit at sunrise. So to this day people say there is smoke to be seen rising from the top of Mount Fuji to the clouds.

THE WONDERFUL PEAR-TREE

(CHINESE)

Once upon a time a countryman came into the town on market day and brought a load of very special pears with him to sell. He set up his barrow in a good corner and soon had a great crowd around him, for everyone knew he always sold extra fine pears. Although he did also ask an extra high price. Now, while he was crying up his fruit, a poor, old, ragged, hungry-looking priest stopped just in front of the barrow and very humbly begged him to give him one of the pears. But the countryman, who was very mean and very nasty tempered, wouldn't hear of giving him any, and as the priest didn't seem inclined to move on, he began calling him all the bad names he could think of. 'Good sir,' said the priest, 'you have got hundreds of pears on your barrow. I only ask you for one. You would never even know you had lost one. Really, you needn't get angry.'

'Give him a pear that is going bad; that will make him happy,' said one of the crowd. 'The old man is quite right; you'd never miss it.'

'I've said I won't, and I won't,' cried the countryman: and all the people close by began shouting, first one thing, and then another, until the constable of the market, hearing the hubbub, hurried up; and when he had made out what was the matter, he pulled some cash out of his purse, bought a pear, and gave it to the priest. For he was afraid that the noise would come to the ears of the mandarin who was just being carried down the street.

* * *

The old priest took the pear with a low bow, and held it up in front of the crowd, saying, 'You all know that I have no home, no parents, no children, no clothes of my own, no food, because I gave everything up when I became a priest. So it puzzles me how anyone can be so selfish and so stingy as to refuse to give me one single pear. Now, I am quite a different sort of man from this countryman. I have got here some perfectly exquisite pears, and I shall feel most deeply honoured if you will accept them from me.'

'Why on earth didn't you eat them yourself, instead of begging for one?' asked a man in the crowd.

'Ah,' answered the priest, 'I must grow them first.' So he ate the pear, only leaving a single pip. Then he took a pick which was fastened across his back, dug a deep hole in the ground at his feet, and planted the pip, which he covered all over with earth. 'Will someone fetch me some hot water to water this?' he asked.

The people, who were crowding around, thought he was only joking. But one of them ran and fetched a kettle of boiling water and gave it to the priest, who very carefully poured it over the place where he had sowed the pip. Then while he was pouring they saw first a tiny green sprout, and then another, pushing their heads above the ground. Then one leaf uncurled, and then another, while the shoots kept growing taller and taller. Then there stood before them a young tree with a few branches and a few leaves, then more leaves then flowers, and last of all, clusters of huge, ripe, sweet-smelling pears weighing the branches down to the ground! Now the priest's face shone with pleasure, and the crowd roared with delight when he picked the pears one by one until they were all gone, handing them around with a bow to each man present. Then, the old man took the pick again, and hacked at the tree until it fell with a crash. When he shouldered it, leaves and all, with a final bow, he walked away.

All the time this had been going on, the countryman, forgetting his barrow and pears, had been in the midst of the crowd standing on the tips of his toes and straining his eyes to try to make out what was happening. But when the old priest had gone and the crowd was getting thin, he turned round to his barrow and saw with horror that it was quite empty. Every single pear was gone! In a moment he understood what had happened. The pears the old priest had been so generous in giving away were not his own; they were the countryman's! What was more, one of the handles of his barrow was missing, and there was no doubt that he had started from home with two! He was in a towering rage and rushed as hard as he could after the priest; but just as he turned the corner, he saw lying close to the wall the barrow-handle itself, which without a doubt was the very pear-tree which the priest had cut down. All the people in the market were simply splitting their sides with laughter; but as for the priest, no one saw him anymore.

MANGITA AND LARINA

(FILIPINO)

This is a tale told in the lake district of Luzon. At times of rain or in winter the waters of the Laguna de Bai rise and detach from the banks a peculiar vegetation that resembles lettuce. These plants, which float for months down the Pasig River, gave rise, no doubt, to the story.

Many years ago there lived on the banks of the Laguna de Bai a poor fisherman whose wife had died, leaving him two beautiful daughters named Mangita and Larina.

Mangita had hair as black as night and dark skin. She was as good as she was beautiful, and was loved by all for her kindness. She helped her father mend the nets and make the torches to fish with at night, and her bright smile lit up the little nipa house like a ray of sunshine.

Larina was fair and had long golden hair of which she was very proud. She was different from her sister, and never helped with the work, but spent the day combing her hair and catching butterflies. She would catch a pretty butterfly, cruelly stick a pin through it, and fasten it in her hair. Then she would go down to the lake to see her reflection in the clear water, and would laugh to see the poor butterfly struggling in pain. The people disliked her for her cruelty, but they loved Mangita very much. This made Larina jealous, and the more Mangita was loved, the more her sister thought evil of her.

One day a poor old woman came to the nipa house and begged for a little rice to put in her bowl. Mangita was mending a net and Larina was combing her hair in the doorway. When Larina saw the old woman she spoke mockingly to her and gave her a push that made her fall and cut her head on a sharp rock; but Mangita sprang to help her, washed the blood away from her head, and filled her bowl with rice from the jar in the kitchen.

The poor woman thanked her and promised never to forget her kindness, but to her sister she spoke not a word. Larina did not care, however, but laughed at her and mocked her as she painfully made her way again down the road. When she had gone Mangita took Larina to task for her cruel treatment of a stranger; but, instead of doing any good, it only caused Larina to hate her sister all the more.

Some time afterwards the poor fisherman died. He had gone to the big city down the river to sell his fish, and had been attacked with a terrible sickness that was raging there.

The girls were now alone in the world.

Mangita carved pretty shells and earned enough to buy food, but, though she begged Larina to try to help, her sister would only idle away the time.

The terrible sickness now swept everywhere and poor Mangita, too, fell ill. She asked Larina to nurse her, but the latter was jealous of her and would do nothing to ease her pain. Mangita grew worse and worse, but finally, when it seemed as if she would soon die, the door opened and the old woman to whom she had been so kind came into the room. She had a bag of seeds in her hand, and taking one she gave it to Mangita, who soon showed signs of being better, but was so weak that she could not give thanks.

The old woman then gave the bag to Larina and told her to give a seed to her sister every hour until she returned. She then went away and left the girls alone.

Larina watched her sister, but did not give her a single seed.

Instead, she hid them in her own long hair and paid no attention to Mangita's moans of pain.

The poor girl's cries grew weaker and weaker, but not a seed would her cruel sister give her. In fact, Larina was so jealous that she wished her sister to die.

When at last the old woman returned, poor Mangita was at the point of death. The visitor bent over the sick girl and then asked her sister if she had given Mangita the seeds. Larina showed her the empty bag and said she had given them as directed. The old woman searched the house, but of course could not find the seeds. She then asked Larina again if she had given them to Mangita. Again the cruel girl said that she had done so.

Suddenly the room was filled with a blinding light, and when Larina could see once more, in place of the old woman stood a beautiful fairy holding the now well Mangita in her arms.

She pointed to Larina and said, 'I am the poor woman who asked for rice. I wished to know your hearts. You were cruel and Mangita was kind, so she shall live with me in my island home in the lake. As for you, because you tried to do evil to your good sister, you shall sit at the bottom of the lake forever, combing out the seeds you have hidden in your hair.' Then, she clapped her hands and a number of elves appeared and carried the struggling Larina away.

'Come,' said the fairy to Mangita, and she carried her to her beautiful home, where she lives in peace and happiness.

As for Larina, she sits at the bottom of the lake and combs her hair. As she combs a seed out, another comes in, and every seed that is combed out becomes a green plant that floats out of the lake and down the Pasig.

And to this day people can see them, and know that Larina is being punished for her wickedness.

MAKOTA RADJA-RADJA*

(MALAY)

Kings, who are of the true faith, who have wisdom and follow justice, cause men worthy of their confidence to travel through their kingdom, to serve as their eyes and ears, and to make reports on the state and condition of their subjects, so that, knowing the cause, they may examine for themselves the conduct of the servants of God. But there are kings who do not rest contented with the report of their servants, and go themselves by night to see the condition and hear the complaints of subjects. Then they make by day a thorough examination of the matters thus come to their knowledge, in order to regulate them with justice and equity.

A story will illustrate this. Zeyd Ibries Selam tells what follows: The prince of the believers, the Caliph Omar (may God be satisfied with him!), judged the servants of God with equity during the day, and after pronouncing his judgments, he went out of the city on the side toward the cemetery called Bakia-el-Gharkada. There he cut stone to gain money enough for the maintenance of his house, and when night had come, he went through the city to know the good and evil of the servants of God. One night, says Zeyd Ibries Selam, 'I accompanied the prince of the believers, Omar.' When he was outside of Medina, he perceived a fire in an out of the way place, and turned his

---

* Or, 'The Crown of Kings.'

steps thither. Scarcely had he arrived when he heard a woman with three children, and the latter were crying. The woman said, 'O God the most high, I beseech thee, make Omar suffer what I am suffering now.

'He sleeps satiated with food while I and my children are starving.' The prince of the believers, Omar, hearing these words, went to the woman and with a salutation said, 'May I approach?'

The woman answered, 'If it be by way of goodness, come.'

He approached her and questioned her about her situation.

The woman said, 'I come from a far place, and as it was dark when I arrived here I could not enter the city, so I stopped at this place. My children and I are suffering from hunger and we cannot sleep.'

The Caliph inquired, 'What is there in this kettle?'

The woman answered, 'Nothing but water. I put it in the kettle so that the children should imagine that I was cooking rice. Then, perhaps, they would go to sleep and stop crying so loudly.'

As soon as Omar had heard these words he returned promptly to the city of Medina. Arriving at a shop where they sold flour, he bought some and put it into a sack. In another shop he bought some meat. Then lifting the sack to his shoulders he carried it out of the city. I said to him, 'O prince of the believers, give me this sack, that I may carry it for you.'

'If you bear the weight of this sack,' said his glorious Majesty to me, 'who will bear the weight of my fault, and who will clear me from the prayer of this woman in the affliction of her heart when she complained to the Lord of my negligence?'

Omar, having said these words, continued to walk in tears until he had come near the woman and her children. Then he gave her the flour and the meat, and they ate till their hunger was appeased. The woman with a satisfied heart cried, 'May God the most high hear my prayer and render you benefits, since you are so full of compassion for the servants of God and are so much better than Omar.'

The Caliph said to her, 'O woman, blame not Omar, for he knew not how you fared.'

There was once a king in the country of Syria named Malik-us-Saleh. He was very pious and just and continually preoccupied with the state of his subjects. They say that every night he went to the mosque, cemeteries, and other solitary places in search of strangers, fakirs, and poor people who had neither home nor family. One night, arriving near a mosque, he heard the voice of a man inside the edifice. He entered and saw a fakir there. He could not see him distinctly, because he was covered with a mat. But he heard him, and this is what he said: 'O Lord, if on the judgment day thou shalt give a place in heaven to kings who are forgetful of the fakirs and the poor, then O Lord, grant that I may not enter there.'

Malik-us-Saleh, hearing these words, shed tears. He placed a piece of stuff before the fakir with 100 tahil of silver, and said to him:

'O fakir, I have learned from the glorious prophet (may peace be with him!) that fakirs become kings in heaven, after a life of self-sacrifice on earth. Since I am King in this perishable world, I come to you with the weakness of my nature and baseness of my being. I ask you to be at peace with me, and to show yourself compassionate to me when the moment of your glory in heaven shall have arrived.'

When the Sultan Zayed sat upon the royal throne of Irak, the country was infested with malefactors, brigands, robbers, assassins, and the like. The compounds were destroyed, the houses pillaged, and the people killed. The inhabitants could not sleep a single night in quiet, nor pass a single day in safety at home. A crowd of people came with their complaints to the Sultan Zayed, saying, 'The compounds are destroyed, the houses are pillaged, and the men are killed.' All throughout Irak one heard nothing but reports of this kind.

One Friday the Sultan went to the mosque to pray. He then shut all the doors and said to the people in the mosque, 'O servants of God now present in this mosque, know that a duty is imposed upon me. I must protect my subjects, for I shall have to give an account of my actions on the day of judgment. There are now in this country large numbers of malefactors, and many of my people have been ruined by them. It is my duty to repress these disorders. So, then, listen to what I have to say, and repeat it to those who are not present. I swear to you that all who shall three days from now leave his house after the hour of evening prayer, shall be put to death.'

When the three days had passed and the fourth night arrived, Sultan Zayed mounted his horse and traversed the city with an escort of cavaliers. Outside of the city he came to a place and saw a man standing under a tree in the middle of a flock of sheep and goats. He said to him, 'Who are you?'

The man said: 'I come from a far-off village, and I am bringing sheep and goats to the city to sell them, and with their price to buy what I can for my wife and children. When arrived at this place I was so tired that I could not enter the city, and was obliged to stay here, with the intention of entering at daybreak and selling my sheep and goats.'

Sultan Zayed, having heard this response, said: 'Your words are true, but what can I do? If I do not put you to death tomorrow, when the news spreads, they will say Sultan Zayed is not faithful to his word. They will regard me with disdain, and no one will obey my orders. The wicked ones will commit violent acts upon the good ones, and my country will be ruined. Heaven is better for you than this world.' So he had him put to death and ordered that they should take his head.

During that same night all that he met were killed and beheaded. They say that in the course of that first day 500 persons were put to death. At dawn he had all these heads exposed on the highways, and published this proclamation:

'Whosoever shall not obey the commands of Sultan Zayed shall suffer the same fate.'

When the people of the country saw these heads exposed at all sides on the earth, they were frightened, and a respectful fear of Sultan Zayed filled all hearts.

The second night Sultan Zayed went out again from the city, and that night 500 persons were killed.

The third night he remained out of the city till morning, but he did not meet a soul.

The following Friday Sultan Zayed went to the mosque, said his prayers, and declared: 'O servants of God, let no one after today shut the door of his house nor his shop. I take upon myself the charge of replacing those of your goods which shall be destroyed or stolen.'

They all obeyed his orders, for they feared him greatly. Their doors remained opened for several nights, and they never suffered the slightest loss. But after a while a man complained to the Sultan, saying, 'Last night someone stole from me 400 tahil.'

The Sultan said: 'Can you swear to it?'

The man swore to the facts, and the Sultan had 400 tahil counted out to him in place of those he had lost. The following Friday, after prayers, forbidding anyone to leave the mosque, the Sultan said: 'O servants of the Lord, know that 400 tahil have been stolen from the shop of a certain man. Unless you denounce the robber, not one of you shall escape, but today shall all of you be put to death.'

Now, as he had rigorously commanded attendance at Friday's prayer service, the whole town had come to the mosque. They were seized with fright, for they knew that the Sultan kept his word, and they denounced the robber. The latter gave back the 400 tahil and received his punishment.

A long time afterward the Sultan Zayed asked, 'At what place in my kingdom do they fear robbers most of all?'

'In the Valley of the Beni Ardou, in the country of Bassrah, for there they are numerous.'

Sultan Zayed one day had the highways and paths of the valley strewn with gold and silver, precious stones, and stuffs of great price. All these things lay there a long time and not one was taken. Then the Sultan ordered them to take up these riches and give them to the fakirs and the poor. Then he rendered thanks unto God that he had thus securely established his law among his subjects.

Now it was in the times when Nushirvan governed with justice and equity, protecting his subjects and causing his kingdom to prosper. One day he asked the grandees of his court, 'Are there in my kingdom any places deserted and without inhabitants?'

The grandees who were there answered, 'O king of the world, we know not in all your Majesty's realm a place which is not inhabited.'

Nushirvan kept silence, and for many days did not leave the palace. He summoned to his private chamber a learned doctor named Bouzor Djambour, and said to him:

'I desire to know with certainty if all parts of my realm are peopled, or if there are any which are not. How can I be sure of this?'

'To have your Majesty's desire fully satisfied you have only to abstain from leaving the palace.'

Saying this, Bouzor Djambour took leave of the King and went to the audience chamber of the King. He spoke to those assembled there as follows: 'O ministers, generals, and all present, know that his Majesty is ill. Now, in order to cure him you must find for me a little bit of earth from a place in ruins and uninhabited. Those who are faithful servants of the King will not hesitate to accomplish immediately this act of devotion in his service, and to start at once in search of the remedy I have named.'

These words were scarcely uttered when men were sent out to search the towns and villages and find some earth from a place in ruins and uninhabited. They found only one house in ruins, and the governor of the town said as follows about it: 'A merchant once established in this dwelling. He died and left much wealth. As none of his heirs came forward, we closed the doors with stones and mortar, waiting for them to arrive. So the house has fallen to ruin.'

Then the people took a little earth from beneath the house and took it to the King, telling him what had happened. Then the King called an assembly and said:

'Know all that my illness proceeded only from my fear that there might be in my kingdom a house in ruins. Now that it has been shown to me that there exists in my whole realm not a single place in ruins, but that the country is well populated, my malady is cured, seeing that my kingdom is in a perfect condition.'

In the time of Nushirvan a man sold his compound to another man. The buyer of this property, while engaged in making repairs, found in the earth many jars filled with gold which someone had buried there. He went immediately to the one who sold him the premises and told him the news. The seller said:

'That gold is not mine, for I did not put it in the ground. I sold you the compound; the discovery that you have made is yours.'

The buyer replied, 'I bought the premises alone. I did not buy gold, so it is yours.' As each refused to take the treasure, they went to the King Nushirvan and recounted the affair to him, saying, 'This gold should be the property of the King.' But King Nushirvan would not take the gold. He asked the two men if they had children. They replied, 'Yes, my lord, we have each a child, a boy and a girl.'

'Well,' said the King, 'marry the girl to the boy, and give them the gold you found.'

In ancient times a King of China fell ill, and as a result of his malady, he lost his hearing. He wept in sorrow over this affliction and grew very thin and pale. His ministers came one day and asked him to tell them in writing his condition. He answered, 'I am not ill, but so weakened by my inquietude and distress that I can no longer hear the words of my subjects when they come to make their complaints. I know not how to act not to be guilty of negligence in the government of my kingdom.'

The ministers then said: 'If the ears of your Majesty do not hear, our ears shall replace those of the King, and we can carry to his Majesty the complaints and regrets of his subjects. Why, then, should his Majesty be so much disturbed over the weakening of his physical forces?'

The King of China answered, 'At the day of judgment it is I, and not my ministers, who will have to render account of the affairs of my subjects. I must therefore myself examine into their complaints and troubles. I am sure that the burden of ruling would be lighter for me if I could have tranquillity of spirit. But my eyes can see, although my ears are deaf.'

And he commanded them to publish this edict, 'All who are victims of injustice must reduce their complaints to writing, and bring them to the King so that he may look into their troubles.'

They tell also the following story: There was formerly in the city of Isfahan, a king whose power and glory had filled him with pride. He commanded his ministers to build him a palace in a certain place. The ministers, with the architects, ordered the slaves to level the ground to form a vast esplanade and this caused all the houses of the neighbourhood to disappear. Among these houses, they say, there was one belonging to an old woman who was very poor and without a family to help her. In spite of her great age, she went to work as well as she could, in different places, but could scarcely exist on her earnings. Her house, near the site that was selected for the new palace, was old and in a tumble-down condition. They tell that one day having gone a long distance to find work she fell ill and remained a long time without being able to return to her house. Then the architects who were building the palace said, 'We must not let this hovel remain standing so near the King's palace.' So they razed the hut, levelled the earth, and finished the palace with all sorts of embellishments.

The King, taking possession of the palace, gave a grand house-warming festival.

Now on this very day it so happened that the old woman returned home. On arriving she could find no traces of her house, and was stupefied. In one hand she held a stick, in the other some dry wood for her fire. On her back she bore a package of rice and herbs for cooking. She was fatigued with a long journey and faint with hunger. When she saw that her house had disappeared, she knew not what to do nor where to go. She burst into tears. The servants of the King drove her away, and as she went, she fell and spilled her rice and herbs and fell down in the mud. In this state of indescribable desolation she exclaimed, 'O Lord, avenge me on these tyrants!'

The old woman had hardly ceased speaking when the voice of some unseen being was heard above her saying, 'O woman, fly quickly from this spot, for the anger of God is advancing upon the King.' In horror she got up and fled in all haste. Again she heard the voice saying, 'O woman, look behind you at the palace.' She looked behind her and saw the palace, the King, and all his ministers and servants engulfed in the bowels of the earth by the will of God. To this day that place vomits fire and smoke as a mark and a warning.

In the Kitab Tarikh, it is told that in ancient times under the kings of Persia named Moah, men were happy because they followed the rules of justice. But after these kings, Yazdegerd-ibn-Shahryar reigned over Persia. By his harsh tyranny, he destroyed the high reputation of the kings of Persia and wretchedly closed a series of reigns lasting 4,000 years and noted all over the world for justice and equity. Under the rule of this miserable tyrant, countless numbers of men perished and a great many prosperous and famous cities were devastated. All the better classes of citizens were plunged into the most frightful distress and the most lamentable desolation, and it would be impossible to tell how great and wide-spread was the mourning. Now, while all were groaning in affliction, the King made merry.

One day in his presumptuous pride he assembled his ministers and his generals to show his royal power and his domination over the people. He was seated on his throne, surrounded by a crowd of courtiers, when suddenly a beautiful horse crossing the city at a gallop went straight into the palace of the King, among the ministers and the grandees. They all admired the beautiful horse, the like of which none had ever seen. Nobody dared to seize him as he pranced from right to left. Suddenly the horse approached the throne and laid down at the feet of the King. The King patted and stroked him, and the horse never moved. Then the wicked King began to laugh and said, 'O my ministers, you see how far my greatness goes. It is only at my throne that this wonderful horse has stopped. I will mount and ride him on the esplanade.' The King ordered a saddle to be brought, and was placing it on the horse with his own hands when he received such a kick over the heart that it immediately killed him. Then the wonderful horse vanished, and no one saw where it went. The people all rejoiced and said, 'Of a truth, this mysterious horse was one of the angels of God sent to exterminate a tyrant.'

It was in the time of this King, and by his tyranny, that the kingdom of the sovereign of Persia was ruled and fell into the hands of another person, King Khochtacab, the most celebrated of all the kings of his time. By his power, greatness, and magnificence, he had raised in rank a man named Rassat Rouchin, a name which in Persia signifies 'sincere and brilliant'. Influenced by this fine name, the King forgot all prudence, and without any proof of his capacity, he raised this man to power and made him minister, turning over to him the care of the most important affairs in his kingdom and giving him all his confidence. His ostensible conduct was irreproachable, and his acts had the appearance of honesty and truth. One day the minister Rassat Rouchin said to the King, 'The people, on account of our leniency and goodness, are forgetting their duty and are showing no more deference nor respect. We must inspire them with fear, or affairs will not prosper.'

The King in his blind confidence responded, 'Do whatever you think is right.' As soon as the minister had come from the palace of the King, he addressed a proclamation to the towns and villages in which he said, 'His Majesty is irritated with his subjects. You must all come with presents to appease his anger.' From all sides arrived princes and ministers and grandees of the realm with precious and magnificent objects. Seized with fear, they sought the counsel of the minister Rassat Rouchin.

'How,' said they, 'dare we present ourselves before his Majesty in his present state of anger against us?'

Then the minister responded, 'If the instant of death has not yet come for you, I will try to save you. I tremble to admit you to the King, but what can I do? On account of the critical situation, I will go alone before the King and present your case.' So every day he conducted them only as far as the door of the King. There they were told of the fines to which they had been condemned. He took what they had, and sent them home.

This sort of thing continued for a long while until the means of the people were exhausted and the treasury became absolutely empty. The King, always full of confidence in the uprightness of the minister, was in complete ignorance of all this. But at that time there was a king who was an enemy of King Khochtacab. When he learned that the subjects of the latter were suffering cruelly from the oppression of his minister and that his generals were weakened by hunger, he took heart and invaded the kingdom. Then King Khochtacab commanded that his treasury should be opened, and that they should take out all the wealth to gratify the army, gain the hearts of the generals, and defray the expenses of the war. But he found that there was nothing left in the treasury. The army, weakened, was incapable of resisting. The King, who shut up in his fort, found it impossible to attack the enemy, and they ravaged and despoiled the kingdom.

The King, having been considered so great, was cruelly wounded by shame at his defeat. He knew not which way to turn his steps. His soul was profoundly troubled. One day, when he had gone forth from the city wandering at random through plain and forest, he saw a shepherd's hut in the distance. At the door were two dogs hanging by the neck. Seeing the King, the shepherd approached and led him to his hovel and served him with the best food he could afford. But the King said, 'I shall not eat until you have told me why you have hanged these two dogs at your cabin door.'

The shepherd responded, 'O king of the world, I hanged these two dogs because they betrayed my flock. As my flock was wasting away, I hid one day to see what took place. The wolf came and the dogs played with him and let him carry off sheep and goats. So I hanged the two dogs as faithless traitors.'

The King returned to the city and thought over this singular story. 'It is a lesson for me,' he said. 'A revelation. It is impossible not to see that my subjects are the flock and I am the shepherd while my minister has acted like the shepherd's dogs, and the enemy who has my kingdom is the wolf. I must examine into the conduct of my minister and see with what fidelity he has served me.'

When he had returned to the palace he called his secretaries and bade them bring the registers in which the accounts of the kingdom were kept. When these registers were opened, he saw that they mentioned only the name of the minister Rassat Rouchin and included such statements as, 'Intercession of Rassat Rouchin in favour of princes so and so, ministers such and such, and grandees this and that, who ask pardon for their faults. Rassat Rouchin took their treasures and granted them grace.' There was nothing else in the registers. When the King saw this he said, 'Who rests his faith upon a name goes often without bread, while he who faithless proves for bread shall lose his soul instead.'

The King had engraved these words in letters of gold and fastened to the gate. And at this gate he had the false minister hanged as the dogs were hanged at the cabin door.

A King of Persia, in a fit of anger against his wife for a certain fault which she had committed, commanded his prime minister to put her to death with her nursing infant. The minister, on account of the furious anger of the King, did not dare to plead the Queen's cause but took her to his mother's house. The minister found another woman who had been condemned to death and had her executed, telling the King that it was the Queen who was beheaded. The King's child grew and flourished until he had become a handsome young man. But the King grew more and more morose and melancholy and shut himself up in the palace. The minister, noticing this continual sadness of the King, said, 'O king of the world, what has come over the heart of your Majesty? Pray tell me the cause of your sorrow.'

And the King said, 'O minister, how should I not be sad and disturbed? Here I am getting old, and I have no son to cause my name to live and protect my kingdom. That is the cause of my sorrow and unhappiness.'

When the minister heard these words he said, 'O king of the world, your sorrow shall not long endure, for you have a son capable of preserving and protecting your kingdom. This son of yours has intelligence, education, natural gifts, and great personal beauty, and is of most excellent character.'

The King said, 'Where is this son of whose existence I have been unaware?'

The minister answered, 'Your Majesty is not aware of his existence, but I know that he is very much alive.' The minister then related how he had spared the lives of the Queen and her child. The King was transported with joy, and cried, 'Happy the king who has such a minister!'

The minister bowed low and said, 'When shall your son, the prince, present himself?'

The King answered, 'Go seek 40 young men of his age, build, figure, and complexion. Have them all dressed alike. Bring these 40 young men with my son to a certain place in the plain. Await for me there, but do not tell this secret to a soul. When I have arrived at the spot then these forty young men will present themselves before me. If my son is among them I shall most certainly recognize him.'

The minister took leave of the King and with a heart filled with joy set about doing what the King had ordered. When the King had arrived at the spot chosen, his minister advanced followed by 41 youths all dressed alike. As soon as the King had seen them he recognized his son and called him to his side. Then he went back to the city with him and all the grandees. The next day he invited the latter to a great festival, and gave to each of them a splendid present. He turned over his kingdom to his son, taking care to place him and his government under the tutelage of the good minister who had saved his wife and brought him up. Then the King went into a religious retreat, and as long as he lived, he occupied himself in the service of God.

The Sultan Alexander, called the Two-Horned, at the beginning of his reign sent an ambassador to King Darius, who was then at the zenith of his greatness. On his return, this ambassador made his report to King Alexander. The latter read it, but he had doubts over a certain word therein contained. He questioned his ambassador about the word, saying, 'Did you hear that exact word from the mouth of King Darius?'

The ambassador replied, 'I heard it with my own ears.'

King Alexander, not being able to believe it, wrote a second letter, mentioning this word, and despatched to King Darius another ambassador, charged to deliver it. When King Darius came to this special word from the letter of King Alexander, he took a knife and cut it out. Then he wrote a letter to King Alexander, in which he said, 'The sincerity of the soul of the King is the foundation of his realm and his greatness. His words, therefore, should be faithfully transmitted and reproduced by his ambassador. I have cut out of your letter a certain word because it was never pronounced by me, and if your former ambassador were only here I would cut out his lying tongue even as I have cut out the word from your letter.'

When this answer of King Darius's was borne to King Alexander he read it and summoned before him the faithless ambassador. 'Why,' said he, 'were you willing, with a word, to cause the loss of many men and countries?'

'Because they showed me little deference and did not treat me well.'

King Alexander said, 'Foolish man! And you thought that we sent you to look after your own personal interests and neglect those of the nation?' He commanded that his tongue should be torn out and made a proclamation saying, 'This is the fate of traitors who falsely report the words of kings.'

In the Kitab Tarikh the following is recounted: The Sultan Homayoun sent an ambassador to the King of Khorasan. When this ambassador, on his arrival in the country, delivered the letter of the Sultan to the King, the latter asked:

'How does your King conduct himself regarding his subjects? How does he govern them?'

'The rule of conduct and the mode of government used by my King are to make himself loved by all his subjects,' answered the ambassador.

The King asked, 'Of what nature is the affection of your King for his subjects?'

'That of a mother and father for their children and grandchildren.'

'In hard and calamitous times, how does your King conduct himself?'

'He shows that he cares not for riches, for the door of his treasury is always open.'

'In the daily receptions, how does your King behave?'

'The receptions of my King resemble the gardens of Paradise refreshed by sweet breezes and scented with the balmy breath of sweetly smelling plants or like a sea filled with pearls and corals.'

The King asked again, 'And in council how speaks your King?'

The ambassador answered, 'All those who hear my King in council become wise if they lack wisdom and brave if they lack courage.'

The King of Khorasan was enchanted with the answers of the ambassador, loaded him with presents, and said to him, 'The spirit and judgment of your King are reflected in the person of his ambassador. They should all be like you.' And he addressed in answer to the Sultan a letter filled with compliments and felicitations.

In the Kitab Tarikh, it is related that the Sultan Mahmoud was fond of his servant Ayaz on account of the excellence of his wit and judgment. The other servants of the Sultan were jealous of Ayaz and murmured against him. One day the ministers and grandees were in the presence of the Sultan Mahmoud, and Ayaz was standing respectfully before him. Someone brought a cucumber as a present to the Sultan. The Sultan sliced it and ate a morsel. He found it very bitter but gave no sign of this. He handed a piece of it to Ayaz, saying, 'Eat some of this cucumber and tell me how it tastes so that the others present may eat some of it also and tell us if they ever ate anything like it.' Ayaz saluted and ate the cucumber with an appearance of pleasure.

'It is very good.'

The King made the others eat of it. They found that it was bitter and were angry with Ayaz and asked how he dare to lie in such a manner.

'It is true,' said the Sultan. 'How could you say it was good?'

Ayaz answered with respect, 'May the Lord bless the king of the world! How many favours have you given me! How many sweet and savoury dainties! How, then, could I make a wry face over one bitter morsel? I ought, on the contrary, to declare that the bitterness of this mouthful is completely annulled by the delicious sweetness of the others, so that your Majesty shall continue to bestow dainties upon me as before.'

A certain king, vain of his royal power, had a servant who was very pious and a true believer, very punctilious in the practice of his religious duties. The King distinguished him above all the others as one in whom he could trust on account of the integrity of his heart. He had given him this order:

'Go not far away from here, day or night. Keep close watch and neglect not my service.' The servant, after finishing his religious duties, took his post, where the King from time to time sent for him. But the King had need of him, and he was not to be found. They sent to look for him, but in vain, and the King grew very angry with him. Finally the servant arrived and prostrated himself before the King. The latter, full of wrath, demanded, 'Why are you late? Why don't you pay attention to my orders?' And he commanded that the man be punished, to make him more attentive to the King's service.

But the servant replied, 'If I am late, it is only on account of the great embarrassment in which I find myself placed.'

'What embarrassment? Tell me.'

The servant, bowing low, spoke as follows, 'My embarrassment comes from the fact that I have two masters to serve. The first is the true Master, he who created the universe and the children of Adam, whose punishments are very severe. The second is only the servant of the former, and not the true Master. I am obliged to attend to the service of the true Master before the service of the second. That is the embarrassment in which I find myself.'

When the King heard these words he shed abundant tears, and said, 'From this day forth you are free. Follow the service of the Lord, and do not forget to pray for me.'

The servants of the King should love their King more than they love their own life, their mother, their father, their children, their grandchildren, their family, their riches, and all that belongs to them. In a word, the person of their King should be above all, so that one may call them true servants of the King, and that in all truth they may be termed his favourites. They tell the story that one day the Sultan Mahmoud Ghazi (may grace be upon him!) was seated on his throne, surrounded by his ministers and his officers, among whom was Ayaz. The Sultan said to his treasurer:

'Go to the treasure-chamber. Take to a certain place gold, silver, precious stones, and other objects of great value. For we are going there to amuse ourselves and present these treasures to those who shall accompany us.'

One day the Sultan started to go and amuse himself at that place, and as soon as the news spread abroad, a great number of people followed him there. When he arrived, he halted at a spot level, clean, and well lighted, and said to his treasurer:

'Expose my treasures here, in this place, so that all those who are happy shall obtain a present according to their degree of happiness, and that one may know who are those who have the most luck and those who have the least.'

All hearing these words quickly approached, pressing forward, with their eyes wide open and their looks fixed on the treasurer, praying him to exhibit the presents at the designated place. At this very moment the Sultan spurred his horse to a gallop and rode from their presence. When he was far away and out of their sight, he stopped and looked behind him. There he saw Ayaz, the only one who had followed him. The others, preoccupied with getting their share of the treasures, never suspected that the Sultan had gone and was already far away from them. The Sultan, halting a moment, returned to the city.

On their side, the ministers and the grandees, having taken possession of the most precious objects, returned joyfully to their homes. On the way they compared notes with each other about their shares of the treasure. One said, 'I had the best luck,' and another, 'No, I had the best.' And all, whoever they were, said the same thing, for all except Ayaz had their share of the King's presents. So they said among themselves, 'It is clear that the one who has no luck is Ayaz.'

Some jealous ones added, 'In truth, Master Ayaz has no luck at all. By his lack of intelligence and good judgment he has had none of the Sultan's presents.'

Ayaz heard all these remarks, but kept silent. Some days later, the Sultan came out of his palace and sat upon the throne. All the grandees came into his presence. Ayaz was standing before him. The Sultan asked:

'Who among you had no luck?'

The ministers answered, 'It is Ayaz! He did not get a single one of your Majesty's many presents. It is clear that he has no luck, for he left all those precious objects and came back with empty hands.'

The Sultan said: 'O Ayaz, are our presents without value in your eyes, that you disdain them? I don't know why you took nothing that was within your grasp. You would have prevented them from saying that you have no luck. What was your motive in doing a thing that has the approbation of nobody?'

Ayaz responded, 'May the days and prosperity of the King increase! May the presents never tarnish that he has given to his servants. As for me, I have more luck than those who received the presents of your Majesty.'

The Sultan said, 'O Ayaz, prove to me the truth of your words.'

Ayaz responded, 'If they found some part in the largesse which were given them, I found the author himself of those great gifts. If they found gold, I found the master of the gold. If others found silver, I found the master of silver. If others found precious stones, I found the master of precious stones. If others yet found some pearls, I found the ocean of pearls. Who, therefore, O king of the world, among all those who vaunt themselves as having luck, has more than I have?'

The Sultan replied, 'O Ayaz, tell me what is the meaning of your words. Where is all that which you say you found?'

Ayaz responded, 'May the most high protect the person of the king of the world, more precious to me than all those objects of price! In whatever place may be his august person, there I am, and I thus obtain all that my heart desires. When I am with your Majesty, and your Majesty is with me, what do I lack? Who, then, has more luck than I have?'

One day the Sultan Alexander was plunged in sadness, and kept himself shut up in his palace. The wise Aristotle came before him, and seeing him absorbed in sad thoughts, asked him:

'Why is the Sultan so sad and what keeps him from going out of his palace?'

The Sultan Alexander answered: 'I am grieving at the thought of the smallness of this world, and of all the troubles I am giving myself and others for the sake of reigning over a world that is of so little worth. It is the vanity of my works that renders me sad.'

Aristotle replied: 'The reflection of the Sultan is just, for what, in truth, is the world? Certainly it has not enough importance by itself that the Sultan should occupy himself with a vain kingdom. But the government of this world is a mark of the sublime and eternal kingdom of the other world, and this kingdom the Sultan can obtain by governing this present world with justice. Your Majesty must therefore give all his cares to the government of this world, to obtain finally in the other world a kingdom of which the greatness is beyond measure and the duration is eternal.' The Sultan Alexander heard with pleasure the words of his wise counsellor.

Two qualities are essential to kings, generosity and magnanimity. When a minister remarks, in his king, sentiments unworthy of his rank, he should warn him of the fact, and should turn him from unworthy actions. They tell that a king, having made a gift of 500 dirhams, his minister said to him, 'I have heard from the mouth of wise men that it is not permitted to kings to make a present of less than 1,000 dirhams!'

One day Haroun-al-Rashid made a gift of 500 tahil. His minister, named Yahya, made by signs and by gestures every effort to prevent him from doing this. When all those who had been present were gone, Haroun-al-Rashid said:

'O Yahya! What were you trying to do with all your signs?'

The latter replied: 'O prince of true believers! I was trying to say that kings should never let it be seen that they are capable of making presents of less than 1,000 dirhams.'

One day King Mamon-al-Rashid heard his minister, named Abbas, say to a servant, 'Go to the bazaar and buy something with this half-tahil.'

Mamon-al-Rashid was angry with him and said, 'You are capable of dividing a tahil in two! That is not proper in a minister; you are not worthy of the name,' and he forthwith disposed him from office.

In the Kitab Sifat-el-Molouk it is related that the King Chabour, giving his last instructions to his son, said as follows: 'O my son! Whenever you make a present to anyone, do not bestow it with your own hands. Do not even examine or have brought into your own presence the gifts that you make. Whenever you give a present, see that it be at least the equivalent of the revenue of a town in value, so that it will enrich the recipients and make them and their children and grandchildren free from adversity. Furthermore, my child, beware all your life of giving yourself up to operations of commerce in your kingdom. For this kind of affair is unworthy of a king who has greatness of character, prosperity, and birth.'

King Harmuz received one day a letter from his minister in which he said, 'Many merchants being in town with a great quantity of jewels, pearls, hyacinths, rubies, diamonds, and other precious stones, I bought all they had for your Majesty, paying 200,000 tahil. Immediately afterward there arrived some merchants from another country who wanted to buy these and offered me a profit of 200,000 tahil. If the King consents I will sell the jewels and later buy others.'

King Harmuz wrote to his minister the following response:

'What are 200,000 tahil? What are 400,000 tahil, profit included? Is that worth talking about and making so much? If you are going into the operations of commerce who will look after the government? If you buy and sell, what will become of the merchants? It is evident that you would destroy thus our good renown and that you are the enemy of the merchants of our kingdom, for your designs would ruin them. Your sentiments are unworthy of a minister.' And for this he removed him from office.

In the Kitab Sifat-el-Houkama it is said, 'There is a great diversity of inclinations among men. Everyone has his own propensity. One is borne naturally toward riches, another toward patience and resignation, another toward study and good works. And in this world the humours of men are so varied that they all differ in nature. Among this infinite variety of dispositions of soul, that which best suits kings and ministers is greatness of character, for that quality is the ornament of royalty.

One day the minister of the Sultan Haroun-al-Rashid was returning from the council of state to his house when he was approached by a beggar who said: 'O Yahya! Misery brings me to you. I pray you give me something.'

When Yahya had arrived at his house, he made the beggar sit down at the door, and an attendant said to him:

'Every day give this man 1,000 dinars, and for his food give him his part in the provisions consumed in your house.'

They say that for a month the beggar came every day and sat at Yahya's door, and received the sum of 1,000 dinars.

At the end of the month he had received a total of 30,000 dinars, and the beggar went away. When informed of his departure, Yahya said, 'By the Lord! If he had not gone away and had come to my door for the rest of his life, I should have given him the same daily ration.'

In the Kitab Tarikh the following is told: There was once upon a time a Persian king named Khosrow, remarkable among all the kings of Persia for his power, his greatness of character, his goodness, and the purity of his morals. His wife, named Shirin, was of a rare beauty, and no one at that time could be compared to her, for she possessed all the virtues. Khosrow passionately loved Shirin. Among the books, which speak of loving couples, there is one called 'Khosrow and Shirin'. One day Khosrow was seated in the palace with his wife Shirin when a fisherman brought in a fine fish as a present to Khosrow. The latter ordered them to give him a present of 4,000 dirhams.

'You are wrong,' said Shirin.

'And why?' asked the King.

'If, in the future, you made one of your servants a present of 4,000 dirhams he will not fail to say forthwith, "I am considered as the equal of a fisherman." If your present is less than 4,000 dirhams, then necessarily he will say, "I am considered as being less than a fisherman," and your actions will sadden his heart.'

Khosrow said, 'Your observation is just. But I have spoken, and I cannot reverse what I have said, for it is shameful for a king to fail in keeping his word.'

Shirin replied, 'Never mind, I know a way, and no one can say that you broke your promise.'

'What is this way?' asked Khosrow.

Shirin answered, 'Put this question to the fisherman, "Is this a fresh-water or a salt-water fish?"

'If he answers, "It is a fresh-water fish," say, "I want a salt-water one," and the contrary. Then he will go away and you will be released from your foolish promise.'

Khosrow, who by love of Shirin could not help hearing her advice and following it, put the question to the fisherman. But the latter, suspecting a trap, said, 'It is both.' King Khosrow began to laugh, and gave him 4,000 dirhams in addition.

'The fisherman, having received his 8,000 dirhams, put them in a sack and went away. On the journey, a dirham fell to the ground, and the fisherman, lowering his sack, began to search for the dirham that had fallen. When he found it, he placed it with the others and took up his march again.

Khosrow and Shirin had both been witnesses of his action. Shirin said to Khosrow, 'Behold the baseness and the lack of judgment of the fisherman. He wearied himself to hunt for one dirham when he had a sack full of them. Recall him and do him shame.'

Khosrow, who from his love for Shirin was incapable of resisting her words and always obeyed them, recalled the fisherman and said to him, 'Of a truth, you have a low soul, and possess neither judgment nor dignity. What! One of your 8,000 dirhams was lost and you deferred your journey until you had found it? That shows the baseness of your soul and your lack of judgment.'

The fisherman made obeisance and answered, 'May the prosperity of the king of the world increase! I sought not the dirham on account of its money value, but only on account of the greatness and importance of the words engraved upon the coin. On one of its sides is written the name of God most high. On the other side is written the name of the King. Had I not found the dirham and had left it on the ground, then people passing would have trodden upon it. The two names inscribed upon it, which ought to be glorified by all men, would have been despised and disgraced, and I would have been the accomplice of all the passers-by who trod upon it. That is why I took the trouble to find the dirham.'

Khosrow was pleased with this answer and gave him still another 4,000 dirhams. The fisherman, filled with joy, took his 12,000 dirhams and returned to his home.

A man had committed a serious offence against King Haroun-al-Rashid. Condemned to death, he succeeded in escaping. But, he had a brother. The King summoned the latter and said to him, 'Find your brother, so that I may kill him. If you do not find him, I will kill you in his place.' This man did not find his brother, so the King Mamon-al-Rashid ordered one of his servants to bring him to be killed. But this servant said, 'O prince of believers! If the one who received the command to put this man to death brings him for that purpose and at the same time a messenger comes from your Majesty with an order not to kill him, ought he not to release him?'

King Mamon-al-Rashid answered, 'He certainly ought to release him on account of my orders.'

'O prince of believers,' answered the servant, 'The Koran says, "He who has a burden shall not bear another's."'

Then the King said, 'Set the man free, for this must cover his case, and means that the innocent should not perish for the guilty.'

They tell that a pundit appeared one day before the Sultan Ismail Samani, King of the country of Khorasan. The Sultan received him with great distinction, and at his departure, saluted him most respectfully and escorted him to the door taking seven steps behind him.

The next night he dreamed that the glorious prophet (with whom be peace!) spoke thus to him: 'O Ismail, because you honoured one of my pundits, I will pray to God that your seven children and grandchildren shall become great and glorious kings.' They say that for many years, the kingdom of Khorasan flourished under the paternal government of the successors of this Sultan.

The Sultan Abdallah Tahir, as soon as he had taken possession of the throne of Khorasan, received the homage of a large number of his subjects. At the end of several days he asked, 'Is there anyone of distinction in the country who has not come to present himself before me?' They told him, 'There are two people that have not come, one named Ahmed Arab, and the other named Mahomet Islam. But these two men never present themselves before kings and ministers.'

The Sultan replied, 'Since they will not come to find kings and ministers, I must go to them.' So one day the Sultan repaired to the house of Ahmed Arab. The latter, immediately arising, remained standing a long time facing the Sultan. Then regarding him fixedly he said to him, 'O Sultan, I had people heard tell of your beauty, and I now see that they spoke the truth. Make not of that body the embers of hell.' Saying this he returned to his prayers. The Sultan Abdallah Tahir went away from the sheik's house weeping.

He then took himself to the house of Mahomet Islam. At the news that the Sultan was coming to see him, the sheik shut the door of his house, saying, 'I ought not to see him. I ought not to speak to him.'

The Sultan departed in tears and said, 'Friday, when the sheik goes to the mosque I will go to him.'

When Friday came, he was on horseback surrounded by soldiers awaiting the arrival of the sheik. As soon as he perceived him, he dismounted, approached him on foot, and saluted him. The sheik asked, 'Who are you? What do you want of me?'

The Sultan answered, 'It is I, Abdallah Tahir. I have come to see the sheik.'

The latter, turning away his face, said to the Sultan, 'What connection is there between you and me?'

The Sultan fell at the feet of the sheik, in tears, in the middle of the highway and invoking God the most high, spoke as follows, 'O Lord, forgive my faults, on account of the many virtues of this faithful sheik.' He was forgiven and became a good man.

The imam El-Shafei (may mercy be with him!), going from the city of Jerusalem to the country of Egypt, halted in a town called Ramla. One of the inhabitants of this town took him into his house and entertained him with many attentions. The companions of the imam El-Shafei perceived that he felt a certain inquietude, but none of them knew the reason for it. The more the master of the house showered his attentions and civilities, the more disturbed the imam seemed to be. Finally at the moment when the imam was mounting his horse to continue his journey, the master of the house arrived and put a writing into his hands. On reading this, the imam lost his worried air, and giving orders to pay the man 30 dinars, he went on his way rejoicing. One of his companions asked him, 'Why were you so disturbed? What did the writing say? And why did you show so much joy in reading it?'

The imam El-Shafei answered, 'When our host took us to his house I noticed that his face lacked the characteristic signs of honesty. But as he treated us so well, I began to think perhaps I was mistaken in judging him. But when I read the writing he handed me, I saw it was as follows, "While the imam has been here I have spent on him ten dinars. He ought therefore to pay me back 20." So then I knew that I had made no error in reading his character, and was pleased at my skill.'

The story is told that one day as the prophet Solomon was seated on his royal throne surrounded by men, spirits, and birds, two women came before him each claiming possession of a child. These two women kept saying, 'It is my child,' but neither could give proof. All their arguments amounting to nothing, the prophet Solomon commanded that the child should be cut in two, and that each woman should take half. When the executioner advanced, drawing his sword, one of the women bursting into sobs cried out in anguish, 'O Prophet Solomon, don't kill the child. Give it to this woman, it is all I ask!'

As the murder of the child never drew a tear nor a movement of anxiety from the other woman, Solomon commanded them to give it to the woman who had wept because her tears proved her to be the true mother and that the child belonged to her, not to the other woman. Thus did King Solomon show his wisdom in judging character.

O you who are magnificent! Listen, I pray you, and hear to what degree of sublimity generosity is lifted. In the Kitab Adab-is-Solathin it is said that two qualities were given by God in all their perfection to two men; justice to Sultan Nushirvan, King of Persia, and generosity to a subject of an Arab sultan named Hatim-Thai. The author of that work says that in the time of Hatim-Thai there were three kings celebrated throughout the whole world, and rivals in showing the perfection of generosity the King of Roum, the King of Syria, and the King of Yemen. But none of them were as famous as Hatim-Thai. They became jealous of him and united in hostility toward him. They said, 'We are the kings of vast countries, and shall we suffer a simple subject of an Arab sultan to be counted as more generous than we are?' Each of these kings thought to try Hatim-Thai and destroy him.

The first of the three who attempted the undertaking was the King of Roum. This King said to one of his ministers:

'O minister, I hear tell that there is among the Arabs a man named Hatim-Thai, and that he is reputed the most generous man in the world. I am displeased that my name is not as noted for generosity as his. I want to make a proof and see if his fame is true or false. I have heard that Hatim-Thai possesses a horse which he loves as he does his own soul. Well, we will ask him to give us this beloved horse.'

The minister sent an envoy with suitable presents and a letter to give to Hatim-Thai. He arrived in a great storm of wind and rain which permitted no one to attend to his affairs abroad. It was already night, and Hatim-Thai had made no preparations to receive a guest. But he received the stranger with the marks of the highest respect and greatest cordiality.

'What need brings you here to-night?' he asked.

'Nothing but to visit you,' replied the envoy, and he never mentioned that evening his mission from the King of Roum.

As there was nothing in the house to eat, Hatim-Thai killed his favourite horse and served it for his guest's supper. As soon as it was day, the envoy presented the gifts and the letter from the King of Roum. When he read the passage in the letter where the King asked for the horse which had just been killed, Hatim-Thai turned pale and could not say a word. The envoy, observing him in this state, imagined that he regretted the gift of his horse, and said:

'O Hatim-Thai, if it is not with pleasure that you give your horse to my master, think no more about it, and let me return to my country.'

Hatim-Thai answered: 'O envoy of the King of Roum! If I had a thousand horses like that one I should give them all without a moment's hesitation. But last night I asked you the motive which brought you hither, and you said it was merely to visit me. So I killed the horse for your food, and that is why I am afflicted with sorrow at my lack of foresight.' He sent the envoy back home with many other horses as a gift.

The envoy told the whole story and the King of Roum said, 'The renown of Hatim-Thai is deserved; he is the most generous of men.' He made an alliance of friendship with him, and the fame of Hatim-Thai grew apace.

The second one who tested Hatim-Thai's generosity was the King of Syria. He said, 'How can Hatim-Thai, who lives in the woods and the plains, occupied in pasturing goats, camels, and horses, be more generous than so great a King as I? I will put him to the proof. I will ask for rich presents that he cannot give, and he will be shamed and humiliated before kings and peoples.'

So the King of Syria sent an envoy to Hatim-Thai to ask for 100 very tall, red camels with long manes and black eyes. Camels of this sort are hard to find, only kings having four or five. When the envoy had arrived he told Hatim-Thai what the King of Syria asked of him. Hatim-Thai was full of joy hearing the words of the envoy, and hastened to regale him bountifully with food and drink. Then he searched among his camels, but he found none such as the King of Syria desired. He ordered a search to be made among the peoples of his nation, Arabs and Bedouins, offering a large price. By the will of God a Bedouin succeeded in finding 100, and Hatim-Thai asked only the delay of one month in payment. The envoy returned home with the red camels and many other presents. Seeing them, the King of Syria was struck with astonishment and cried, 'Behold, we wished only to test Hatim-Thai, and now he has gone into debt to satisfy our desire. Yes, truly he is the most generous man in the world.'

He commanded them to send the 100 red camels loaded with magnificent presents back to Hatim-Thai. As soon as they arrived, Hatim-Thai summoned the owner and gave him the camels with all their burden of riches, without keeping anything for himself. When the envoy recounted all these things to the King of Syria, he marvelled and exclaimed, 'No one can equal Hatim-Thai. He is generosity itself, in all its perfection.'

The third king, the King of Yemen, was very generous, and he wanted no one to rival him in this particular. So when he heard of the fame of Hatim-Thai for generosity, he was vexed and full of sorrow. He said, 'How can that poor Hatim be equal in generosity to a great king like me? I give alms to the poor, I feed them, and every day I give them clothing. How is it possible that anyone can dare to mention the name of Hatim-Thai in my presence as the most generous of men?'

Now, at that time an ambassador of the King of Maghreb arrived at the Court of the King of Yemen, who spoke of the wonderful generosity of Hatim-Thai. He felt as if his heart was burning, but did not let his grief appear, and he said to himself, 'Everybody repeats the praises of Hatim, one after another, without knowing exactly who he is, of what birth, and what are the means which permit him thus to give hospitality. I shall cause him to perish.'

The King of Yemen summoned a Bedouin, a bandit celebrated for his ferocity, without pity for the life of a man. The Bedouin arrived, and the King gave him gold, silver, and clothing. 'O Bedouin,' he said to him, 'if you will perform an affair for us, we will give you whatever you ask.'

The Bedouin answered, 'O my lord, king of the world, what is your Majesty's will?'

The King of Yemen replied, 'There is a man named Hatim-Thai, of the tribe of Thai, on the confines of Syria. Go to this country, and employ all the tricks you can to kill him. When you have killed him bring me his head. If you succeed in doing as I wish, whatever you ask, it shall be given you.'

These words of the King filled the Bedouin's heart with joy. He said to himself, 'Here is a good piece of work. For an old tattered cloak I will kill a man. Why then should I hesitate a moment for a superb cloak of scarlet?'

Taking leave of the King, the Bedouin set out promptly and went toward Syria in search of Hatim-Thai. After a while he arrived at a village near to Syria, and there he met a young man of a rare beauty. His face bore the marks of virtue, his language was full of sweetness and affability, his soul was righteous, and his heart compassionate. He asked the Bedouin where he was going. The latter answered, 'I am from the country of Yemen, and am going to Syria.'

The young man replied, 'O my brother! I wish you would do me the favour to rest for a day and a night in my house, and I will do the best to entertain you. After that you shall go on your journey when you wish.'

The Bedouin heard these words with pleasure and went into the young man's house. There he was treated magnificently and regaled so lavishly that he thought he had never seen and eaten so much. He slept peacefully all night. At dawn he said farewell, eager to gain the end of his journey. The young man said to him, 'O my brother, if it is possible, stay two or three days longer. I beg you, so that by my hospitality I may show all the sincere affection that my heart feels for you.'

The Bedouin replied, 'O my brother, truly I would stay longer here, had I not a most important and delicate mission to fulfil. It is impossible for me to stay and enjoy myself here, while I have not yet accomplished my errand.'

The young man answered, 'O my brother, what is this difficult and delicate affair which prevents you from staying here? If you will tell me, surely I shall find some means of coming to your aid, and lightening the burden which weighs so heavily upon your heart. But, now, what can I do since you tell me nothing?'

Hearing these words, the Bedouin kept silence. He said to himself, 'This affair is not easy to execute. It might be of use for me to have a prudent and discreet companion to confer with him about it. Perhaps I should do well to talk of it to this young man and ask his advice.'

And nevertheless he dared not to trust his secret, and his perplexity was written on his countenance. He could not utter a single word and remained very anxious.

The young man observing the state of the Bedouin said to him, 'O servant of God, your embarrassment is evident; you fear to open your heart to me. God alone, in truth, knows the secrets of his servants. But, in your present situation, it may be that I can be of some benefit to you.'

The Bedouin, hearing these words of the young man, said to him, 'O my loyal friend, know then that I am an Arab Bedouin of the country of Yemen; of all the Bedouins of Arabia there is not one so wicked nor so great a thief as I, and that my fame as a bandit is celebrated throughout all Yemen. The King, having resolved upon a wicked deed, ordered his minister to find a man capable of performing it. As I had the reputation of being the greatest bandit of the country of Yemen, I was summoned to the presence of the King. As soon as his Majesty saw me he loaded me with presents and said, "If you do as I wish I will give you many more presents of gold and silver and other magnificent things." I replied, "O my lord, king of the world, what is this affair?"

'You must go and kill a man named Hatim-Thai, who lives on the confines of Syria.' To this I replied, "O my lord, king of the world, I am only a Bedouin, a poor robber, wandering in the forests and the plains. For drink I have but the brackish water of the marshes. For food I have only rats and locusts." On account of my wretchedness, I obeyed the wishes of the King, and promised to execute this affair. But here I am, in a very embarrassing situation, for I do not know this Hatim-Thai, and I don't even know where his tribe is, the Ben-Thai.'

The young man, hearing these words, began to laugh, and said, 'O my brother, be not disturbed. I know this Hatim-Thai, and I will show him to you.' These words rejoiced the Bedouin. The young man continued, 'O my brother, know that the tribe of Ben-Thai inhabit this village, and that the man named Hatim-Thai is himself in this tribe. If you will follow exactly what I indicate to you, you will certainly accomplish your mission.'

The Bedouin answered, 'O my brother, I place my life in your hands. What must be done?'

The young man answered, 'O my brother, there is a place where Hatim-Thai goes for recreation. It is an extremely deserted place, which no one ever visits. When he gets there he eats, drinks, then sleeps with his head covered with a cloth, and his horse tied nearby. When you arrive, you will promptly execute the wish of the King. Then, you will jump upon the horse and dash away from this place and go wherever you like.'

Then the young man went to show the place to the Bedouin, and giving him a poniard with two edges well sharpened, he said, 'O my brother, tomorrow Hatim-Thai will come to this spot. Forget nothing that you have to do.'

All the instructions of the young man were followed by the Bedouin. Early in the morning Hatim-Thai repaired to the designated place. He ate, he drank, and when he had finished his repast he tied his horse nearby. Then, covering his head with a cloth, he fell fast asleep. At this very moment the wicked Bedouin arrived. By the will of God, just as he was about to assassinate the young man, a thought came into his heart. 'Hatim-Thai is celebrated throughout the whole world for his generosity and his benevolence. Before I kill him, while he is still alive, I want to see his face.' And he raised the cloth that covered his head. At the sight of the countenance of the sleeping young man he fell at his feet and covered them with kisses, saying, 'O my friend! What have you done? You ought not to act thus!'

Hearing these words of the Bedouin, the young man said, 'What could I do? For I am the one called Hatim-Thai. The head that the King of Yemen wants is mine. What other means could I employ?' He conducted the Bedouin to his house, regaled him again, and gave him all he needed.

Then the Bedouin took leave and returned to his country. As soon as he arrived in Yemen, he went before the King and recounted all the circumstances relative to Hatim-Thai.

Having heard the story the King shed tears, and said, 'Of a truth, Hatim-Thai is liberal, benevolent, brave, and generous.' Afterward the King of Yemen made a friendship with Hatim-Thai that lasted as long as his life.

When the Sultan Yacoub invaded Khorasan he besieged the capital. Shut up in the city, the Sultan Mahomet made such a strong resistance that for a long time it was impossible to capture the place. But his ministers betrayed him by sending letters to Sultan Yacoub to show how the city might be taken. One only of these ministers, named Ibrahim Hadjib, abstained from sending any traitorous letters, and remained faithful to his master. After a while the city was taken and Sultan Yacoub ascended the throne. Then all the most important people of the country came to pay homage to him. The ministers who had betrayed the former Sultan were conspicuous in their demonstrations of joy. The Sultan Yacoub gave a pleasant reception to those who came, and made them suitable gifts.

After this he asked, 'Who has not come to present himself before me on this day of rejoicing?'

The ministers immediately answered, 'Ibrahim Hadjib is the only one who has not come to present his congratulations.'

Then the Sultan asked, 'Why has he not done so? Is he ill?'

'No,' they answered, 'he is not ill.'

The Sultan summoned Ibrahim Hadjib, and the latter came into the royal presence. The Sultan, observing on his countenance evident marks of care and sorrow, spoke thus to him:

'Ibrahim Hadjib, are you the minister in whom the Sultan Mahomet placed his confidence?' He replied in the affirmative.

'From what motive, Ibrahim Hadjib, did you keep silence and send me no word of advice while the ministers of Sultan Mahomet, now here, sent many letters to show me how to capture the city? Why did you refrain from appearing before me at court today, at the same time with the ministers and grandees? Why, now that you are here, are you the only one to wear a sad and mournful appearance and a long face while all the others show their joy? To all these questions you must truthfully respond. And if you speak not the truth you shall be put to death.'

'If the Sultan wishes to hear the language of truth and will not be vexed by it, I will reply to each of his questions. To the first question, why I sent no letter betraying my King, I will say: Know, Sultan, that the Sultan Mahomet was the King of this country; that he gave me many presents and had full confidence in me, thinking that in the moment of danger I would be his companion and his counsellor. How could I, then, betray him? I knew you not, and had received no benefits from you. Would it have been just for me to send you letters and cause the fall of one who had been so bountiful to me?'

'Your words are just and true,' said the Sultan Yacoub.

Ibrahim Hadjib continued, 'As to the question why I abstained from presenting myself at court today, and why I wore so sorrowful a face, I answer: Know that I could not present myself before the Sultan because he was the enemy of my master and benefactor and brought about the ruin of my lord. That is why I wore a sad face in your presence. Besides, the children and grandchildren of my lord are plunged in grief and anxiety, and how could I be happy in your presence, like these hypocrites, who are very different elsewhere? I have told the truth.'

When the Sultan Yacoub had heard these words of Ibrahim Hadjib, he cried, 'God be praised! Up to this time I have heard tell of ministers, I have seen many kinds, but never have I seen nor heard of a minister like this one. Now, only for the first time have I seen a true minister and listened to the words of truth.' The Sultan Yacoub loaded Ibrahim Hadjib with favours, made him prime minister, and gave him the name of father. As for the other ministers, he caused them to perish with their whole families. Then he published this proclamation:

'Behold the fate of those who are faithless to their promises and commit treason toward their King, for they cannot be counted as men.'

BEEREEUN THE MIRAGE MAKER

(AUSTRALIAN)

Beereeun the lizard wanted to marry Bullai Bullai, the green parrot sisters. But they did not want to marry him. They liked Weedah, the mockingbird better. Their mother said they must marry Beereeun, for she had pledged them to him at their births, and Beereeun was a great wirreenun and would harm them if they did not keep her pledge.

When Weedah came back from hunting they told him what their mother had said, how they had been pledged to Beereeun, who now claimed them.

'Tomorrow,' said Weedah, 'old Beereeun goes to meet a tribe coming from the Springs country. While he is away, we will go towards the Big River and burn the track behind us. I will go out as if to hunt as usual in the morning. I will hide myself in the thick Gidya scrub. You two must follow later and meet me there. We will then cross the big plain where the grass is now thick and dry. Bring with you a firestick; we will throw it back into the plain, and then no one can follow our tracks. On we will go to the Big River. There I have a friend who has a goombeelgah, or canoe. Then shall we be safe from pursuit, for he will put us over the river. And we can travel on and on even to the country of the short-armed people if so we choose.'

The next morning ere Gougourgahgah had ceased his laughter, Weedah had started.

Some hours later, in the Gidya scrub, the Bullai Bullai sisters joined him.

Having crossed the big plain, they threw back a firestick where the grass was thick and dry. The fire sped quickly through it, crackling and throwing up tongues of flame.

Through another scrub went the three, then across another plain, through another scrub and on to a plain again.

The day was hot; Yhi, the sun, was high in the sky. They became thirsty, but saw no water, and had brought none in their haste.

'We want water,' the Bullai Bullai cried.

'Why did you not bring some?' said Weedah.

'We thought you had plenty, or would travel as the creeks run, or at least know of a goolahgool, or water-holding tree.'

'We shall soon reach water. Look even now ahead, there is water.'

The Bullai Bullai looked eagerly towards where he pointed, and there in truth, on the far side of the plain, they saw a sheet of water. They quickened their steps, but the further they went, the further off seemed the water, but on they went ever hoping to reach it. Across the plain they went, only to find on the other side a belt of timber, the water had gone.

The weary girls would have lain down, but Weedah said that they would surely reach water on the other side of the wood. Again they struggled on through the scrub to another plain.

'There it is! I told you so! There is the water.'

And looking ahead they again saw a sheet of water. Again their hopes were raised, and though the sun beat fiercely on them they marched, only to be again disappointed.

'Let us go back,' they said. 'This is the country of evil spirits. We see water, and when we come where we have seen it there is but dry earth. Let us go back.'

'Back to Beereeun, who would kill you?'

'Better to die from the blow of a boondee in your own country than of thirst in a land of devils. We will go back.'

'Not so. He would not kill you with a boondee, but with a gooweera or a poison stick, he would. Your deaths would be slow, and you would be always in pain until your shadow was wasted away. But why talk of returning? Did we not set fire to the big plain? Could you cross that? Waste not your breaths, but follow me. See, there again is water!'

But the Bullai Bullai had lost hope. No longer would they even look up, though time after time Weedah called out, 'Water ahead of us! Water ahead of us!' only to again, and again, disappoint them.

At last the Bullai Bullai became so angry with him that they seized him and beat him. But even as they beat him, he cried all the time, 'Water is there! Water is there!' Then he implored them to let him go, and he would drag up the roots from some water-trees and drain the water from these for them.

'Yonder I see a coolabah; from its roots I can drain enough to quench your thirst. Or here beside us is a bingahwingul; full of water are its roots. Let me go; I will drain them for you.'

But the Bullai Bullai had no faith in his promises, and they beat him the harder until they were exhausted. When they ceased to beat him and let him go, Weedah went on a little way and laid down, feeling bruised all over. He was thankful that the night had come and the fierce sun no longer scorched them.

One Bullai Bullai said to her sister, 'Could we not sing the song our Bargie used to sing, and make the rain fall?'

'Let us try if we can make a sound with our dry throats,' said the other.

'We will sing to our cousin Dooloomai the Thunder; he will hear us and break a rain cloud for us.'

So they sat down, rocking their bodies to and fro, and, beating their knees, sang:

'Moogary, Moogaray, May May, Eehu, Eehu, Doongairah.'

Over and over again they sang these words as they had heard their Bargie, their grandmother do. Then for themselves they added:

'Eehu oonah wambaneah Dooloomai Bullul goonung inderh gingnee Eehu oonah wambaneah Dooloomai.'

Which meant:

'Give us rain, Thunder, our cousin, Thirsting for water are we. Give us rain, Thunder, our cousin.'

As long as their poor parched throats could make a sound, they sang this. Then they lay down to die, weary and hopeless. One said faintly, 'The rain will be too late, but surely it is coming, for strong is the smell of the Gidya.'

'Strong indeed,' said the other. But even this sure sign to their tribe that rain is near did not rouse them; it would come, they thought, too late for them. But even then away in the north a thundercloud was gathering. It rolled across the sky quickly, pealing out thunder calls as it came to tell of its coming. It stopped right over the plain in front of the Bullai Bullai. One more peal of thunder, which opened the cloud, then splashing down came the first big drops of rain. Slowly and few they came until at last, a quick, heavy shower fell, emptying the thunder cloud, and filling the gilguy holes on the plain.

The cool splashing of the rain on their hot, tired limbs gave new life to the Bullai Bullai and Weedah. They all ran to the gilguy holes. Stooping their heads, they drank and quenched their thirst.

'I told you the water was here,' said Weedah. 'You see I was right.'

'No water was here when you said so. If our cousin Dooloomai had not heard our song for his help we should have died, and you too.'

And they were angry. But Weedah dug them some roots, and when they ate, they forgot their anger. When their meal was over, they lay down to sleep.

The next morning, on they went again. That day, across the plains they saw the same strange semblance of water which had lured them on before. They knew not what it could be, only they knew that it was not water.

Just at dusk, they came to the Big River. There they saw Goolayyahlee, the pelican, with his canoe. Weedah asked him to put them over on to the other side. He said he would do so one at a time, as the canoe was small. First he said he would take Weedah, so that he might get a camp ready in the long grass from the bend of the river. He took Weedah over. Then, fastening his canoe, he went up to the Bullai Bullai, who were sitting beside the remains of his old fire.

'Now,' said Goolayyahlee, 'you two will go with me to my camp, which is down in that bend. Weedah cannot get over again. You shall live with me. I shall catch fish to feed you. I have some even now in my camp cooking. There, too, have I wirrees of honey, and durrie ready for the baking. Weedah has nothing to give you but the grass nyunnoos he now is making.'

'Take us to Weedah,' they said.

'Not so,' said Goolayyahlee, and he stepped forward as if to seize them.

The Bullai Bullai stooped and filled their hands with the white ashes of the burnt-out fire, which they flung at him.

Handful after handful they threw at him, until he stood before them white, all but his hands, which he spread out and shook, thus freeing them from the cloud of ashes enveloping him and obscuring his sight.

Having thus checked him, the Bullai Bullai ran to the bank of the river, meaning to get the canoe and cross over to Weedah.

But in the canoe, to their horror, was Beereeun! Beereeun, the one whom they had tried to escape across plain and through scrub.

Yet here he was, while between them and Weedah lay the wide river.

They had not known it, but Beereeun had been near them all the while. He was the one who had made the mirage on each plain, thinking he would lure them on by this semblance of water until they perished of thirst. Dooloomai, their cousin, had saved them from that. But now the chance of Beereeun had come.

The Bullai Bullai looked across the wide river and saw the nyunnoos Weedah had made. They saw him running in and out of them as if he were playing a game, not thinking of them at all. Strange nyunnoos they were too, having both ends open.

Seeing where they were looking, Beereeun said, 'Weedah is womba, deaf. I stole his doowee while he slept and put in its place a mad spirit. He knows naught of you now. He cares naught for you. It happens with those who look too long at the Eer-dheer, or mirage. He will trouble me no more, nor you. Why look at him?'

But the Bullai Bullai could not take their eyes from Weedah. So strangely he went on, unceasingly running in at one end of the grass nyunnoos, through it and out of the other.

'He is womba,' they said, but yet they could not understand it. They looked towards him and called to him, though he heeded them not.

'I will send him far from you,' said Beereeun, getting angry. He seized a spear, stood up in the canoe, and sent it swiftly through the air into Weedah, who gave a great cry, screamed 'Water is there! Water is there!' and fell back dead.

'Take us over! Take us over!' cried the Bullai Bullai.

'We must go to him, we might yet save him.'

'He is all right. He is in the sky. He is not there,' said Beereeun. 'If you want him you must follow him to the sky. Look, you can see him there now.' And he pointed to a star which the Bullai Bullai had never seen before.

'There he is, Womba.'

Across to the grass nyunnoos the Bullai Bullai looked, but no Weedah was there. Then they sat down and wailed a death song, for they knew well they would not ever see Weedah again. They plastered their heads with white ashes and water; they tied on their bodies green twigs. Then, cutting themselves till the blood ran, they lit some smoke branches and smoked themselves, as widows.

Beereeun spoke to Goolayyahlee, the pelican, saying:

'There is no brother of the dead man to marry these women. In this country they have no relation. You shall take one, and I, the other. Tonight when they sleep we will each seize one.'

'That which you say shall be,' said Goolayyahlee the pelican.

But the sisters heard what they said, though they gave no sign and mourned the dead Weedah without ceasing. And with their death song, they mingled a cry to all of their tribe who were dead to help them, and save them from these men who would seize them while they were still mourning before they had swallowed the smoke-water, or their tribe had heard the voice of their dead. As the night wore on, the wailing of the women ceased.

The men thought that they were at length asleep, and crept up to their camp. But lo! it was empty! Gone were the Bullai Bullai!

The men heaped fuel on their fire to light up the darkness, but yet saw no sign of the Bullai Bullai.

They heard a sound, a sound of mocking laughter. They looked round, but saw nothing. Again they heard a sound of laughter. Where did it come from? Again it echoed through the air.

It was from the sky. They looked up. It was the new star Womba, mocking them. Womba, who once was Weedah, laughed aloud to see that the Bullai Bullai had escaped their enemies, for even now they were stealing along the sky towards him, which the men on earth saw.

'We have lost them,' said Goolayyahlee. 'I shall camp alone,' and he turned to go to his dardurr.

'They shall not escape me,' said Beereeun. 'I shall make a roadway to the skies and follow them. Thence shall I bring them back, or wreak my vengeance on them.'

He went to the canoe where his spears were and he also took the spears of Goolayyahlee, which lay by the smouldering fire.

He chose a barbed one. With all his force he threw it up to the sky. The barb caught there, the spear hung down. Beereeun threw another which caught on to the first, and yet another, and so on, each catching the one before it, until he could touch the lowest from the earth. This he clutched hold of, and climbed up, up, up, until he reached the sky. Then he started in pursuit of the Bullai Bullai, and he is still pursuing them.

Since then the tribe of Beereeun have always been able to swarm up sheer heights. Since then too, his tribe, the little lizards of the plains, make the mirages to lure on thirsty travellers, only to send them mad before they die of thirst. Since then Goolayyahlee the pelican has been made white forever after the ashes were thrown by the Bullai Bullai. There are a few black feathers from where he had shaken them off from his hands. The tribe of Bullai Bullai are coloured like the green of the leaves the sisters strung on themselves, in which to mourn Weedah, with here and there a dash of whitish yellow and red caused by the ashes and the blood of their mourning. And Womba, the star – the mad star – still shines. Canopus, we call it. And Weedah, the mockingbird, still builds grass nyunnoos which are open at both ends. In and out of which he runs, as if they were his playground.

And the fire that Weedah and the Bullai Bullai made spread from one end of the country to the other, over ridges and across plains, burned the trees so that their trunks have been black ever since. Deenyi, the iron-barks, smouldered the longest of all, and their trunks were so seared that the seams are deeply marked in their thick black bark still, making them show out grimly distinct on the ridges, to remind the Daens of Beereeun the mirage maker for ever.

HOW THE TIGER GOT HIS STRIPES

(VIETNAMESE)

Once upon a time, ages and ages ago, so long ago that the tiger had no stripes upon his back and the rabbit still had his tail, there was a tiger who had a farm. The farm was very much overgrown with underbrush, and the owner sought a workman to clear the ground for him to plant.

The tiger called all the beasts together and said to them when they had assembled, 'I need a good workman at once to clear my farm of the underbrush. To the one of you who will do this work I offer an ox in payment.'

The monkey was the first one to step forward and apply for the position. The tiger tried him for a little while, but he was not a good workman at all. He did not work steadily enough to accomplish anything. The tiger discharged him very soon, and he did not pay him.

Then the tiger hired the goat to do the work. The goat worked faithfully enough, but he did not have the brains to do the work well. He would clear a little of the farm in one place, and then he would go away and work on another part of it. He never finished anything neatly. The tiger discharged him very soon without paying him.

Next the tiger tried the armadillo. The armadillo was very strong, and he did the work well. The trouble with him was that he had such an appetite. There were a great many ants about the place, and the armadillo could never pass by a sweet tender juicy ant without stopping to eat it. It was lunchtime all day long with him. The tiger discharged him and sent him away without paying him anything.

At last the rabbit applied for the position. The tiger laughed at him and said, 'Why, little rabbit, you are too small to do the work. The monkey, the goat, and the armadillo have all failed to give satisfaction. Of course a little beast like you will fail too.'

However, there were no other beasts who applied for the position so the tiger sent for the rabbit and told him that he would try him for a little while.

The rabbit worked faithfully and well, and soon he had cleared a large portion of the ground. The next day he worked just as well. The tiger thought that he had been very lucky to hire the rabbit. He got tired staying around to watch the rabbit work. The rabbit seemed to know just how to do the work anyway, without orders, so the tiger decided to go away on a hunting trip. He left his son to watch the rabbit.

After the tiger had gone away the rabbit said to the tiger's son, 'The ox which your father is going to give me is marked with a white spot on his left ear and another on his right side, isn't he?'

'Oh, no,' replied the tiger's son. 'He is red all over with just a tiny white spot on his right ear.'

The rabbit worked for a while longer and then he said, 'The ox which your father is going to give me is kept by the river, isn't he?'

'Yes,' replied the tiger's son.

The rabbit had made a plan to go and get the ox without waiting to finish his work. Just as he started off, he saw the tiger returning. The tiger noticed that the rabbit had not worked so well when he was away. After that he stayed and watched the rabbit until the whole farm was cleared. Then the tiger gave the rabbit the ox as he had promised.

'You must kill this ox,' he said to the rabbit, 'in a place where there are neither flies nor mosquitoes.'

The rabbit went away with the ox. After he had gone for some distance, he thought he would kill him. He heard a cock, however, crowing in the distance and he knew that there must be a farm yard near. There would be flies of course. He went on farther and again he thought that he would kill the ox. The ground looked moist and damp and so did the leaves on the bushes. Since the rabbit thought there would be mosquitoes there he decided not to kill the ox. He went on and on and finally he came to a high place where there was a strong breeze blowing. 'There are no mosquitoes here,' he said to himself. 'The place is so far removed from any habitation that there are no flies, either.' He decided to kill the ox.

Just as he was ready to eat the ox, along came the tiger. 'O, rabbit, you have been such a good friend of mine,' said the tiger, 'and now I am so very, very hungry that all my ribs show, as you yourself can see. Will you not be a good kind rabbit and give me a piece of your ox?'

The rabbit gave the tiger a piece of the ox. The tiger devoured it in the twinkling of an eye. Then he leaned back and said, 'Is that all you are going to give me to eat?'

The tiger looked so big and savage that the rabbit did not dare refuse to give him any more of the ox. The tiger ate and ate and ate until he had devoured that entire ox. The rabbit had been able to get only a tiny morsel of it. He was very, very angry at the tiger.

One day not long after, the rabbit went to a place not far from the tiger's house and began cutting down big staves of wood. The tiger soon happened along and asked him what he was doing.

'I'm getting ready to build a stockade around myself,' replied the rabbit. 'Haven't you heard the orders?' The tiger said that he hadn't heard any orders.

'That is very strange,' said the rabbit. 'The order has gone forth that every beast shall fortify himself by building a stockade around himself. All the beasts are doing it.'

The tiger became very much alarmed. 'O, dear! O, dear! What shall I do?' he cried. 'I don't know how to build a stockade. I never could do it in the world. O, good rabbit! O, kind rabbit! You are such a very good friend of mine. Couldn't you, as a great favour, because of our long friendship, build a stockade about me before you build one around yourself?'

The rabbit replied that he could not think of risking his own life by building the tiger's fortifications first. Finally, however, he consented to do it.

The rabbit cut down great quantities of long sharp sticks. He set them firmly in the ground about the tiger. He fastened others securely over the top until the tiger was completely shut in by strong bars. Then he went away and left the tiger.

The tiger waited and waited for something to happen to show him the need of the fortifications. Nothing happened at all.

He got very hungry and thirsty. After a while the monkey passed that way.

The tiger called out, 'O, monkey, has the danger passed?'

The monkey did not know what danger the tiger meant, but he replied, 'Yes.'

Then the tiger said, 'O, monkey, O, good, kind monkey, will you please be so kind as to help me out of my stockade?'

'Let the one who got you in there help you out,' replied the monkey and he went on his way.

Along came the goat and the tiger called out, 'O, goat, has the danger passed?'

The goat did not know anything about any danger, but he replied, 'Yes.'

Then the tiger said, 'O, goat, O, good kind goat, please be so kind as to help me out of my stockade.'

'Let the one who got you in there help you out,' replied the goat as he went on his way.

Along came the armadillo and the tiger called out, 'O, armadillo, has the danger passed?'

The armadillo had not heard of any danger, but he replied that it had passed.

Then the tiger said, 'O, armadillo, O, good, kind armadillo, you have always been such a good friend and neighbour. Please help me now to get out of my stockade.'

'Let the one who got you in there help you out,' replied the armadillo as he went on his way.

The tiger jumped and jumped with all his force to the top of the stockade, but he could not break through. He jumped and jumped with all his might to the front side of the stockade, but he could not break through. He thought that never in the world would he be able to break out. He rested for a little while and as he rested he thought. He thought how bright the sun was shining outside. He thought what good hunting there was in the jungle. He thought how cool the water was at the spring. Once more he jumped and jumped with all his might to the back side of the stockade. At last he broke through. He did not get through, however, without getting bad cuts on both his sides from the sharp edges of the staves. To this day, the tiger has stripes on both his sides.

THE VALIANT CHATTEE-MAKER

(INDIAN)

Long, long ago, in a violent storm of thunder, lightning, wind, and rain, a tiger crept for shelter close to the wall of an old woman's hut. This old woman was very poor, and her hut was a tumble-down place, through the roof of which the rain came drip, drip, drip, on more sides than one. This troubled her much, and she went running about from side to side, dragging first one thing and then another out of the way of the leaky places in the roof. As she did so, she kept saying to herself, 'Oh dear! Oh dear, how tiresome this is! I'm sure the roof will come down! If an elephant, or a lion, or a tiger were to walk in, he wouldn't frighten me half as much as this perpetual dripping.' And then she would begin dragging the bed and all the other things in the room about again, in order to get them out of the way of the rain. The Tiger, who was crouching down just outside, heard all that she said, and thought to himself, 'This old woman says she would not be afraid of an elephant, or a lion, or a tiger, but that this perpetual dripping frightens her more than all. What can this "perpetual dripping" be? It must be something very dreadful.' And, hearing her immediately afterwards dragging all the things about the room again, he said to himself, 'What a terrible noise! Surely that must be the *"perpetual dripping"*.'

At this moment a Chattee-maker, who was in search of his donkey which had strayed away, came down the road. The night being very cold, he had, truth to say, taken a little more toddy than was good for him. Seeing by the light of a flash of lightning, a large animal lying down close to the old woman's hut, he mistook it for the donkey he was looking for. So, running up to the Tiger, he seized hold of it by one ear, and commenced beating, kicking, and abusing it with all his might and main.

'You wretched creature,' he cried. 'Is this the way you serve me, obliging me to come out and look for you in such pouring rain, and on such a dark night as this? Get up instantly, or I'll break every bone in your body.' He went on scolding and thumping the Tiger with his utmost power, for he had worked himself up into a terrible rage. The Tiger did not know what to make of it all, but he began to feel quite frightened, and said to himself, 'Why, this must be the "perpetual dripping"; no wonder the old woman said she was more afraid of it than of an elephant, a lion, or a tiger, for it gives most dreadfully hard blows.'

The Chattee-maker, having made the Tiger get up, got on his back, and forced him to carry him home, kicking and beating him the whole way (for all this time he fancied he was on his donkey), and then he tied his fore feet and his head firmly together, and fastened him to a post in front of his house, and when he had done this, he went to bed.

Next morning, when the Chattee-maker's wife got up and looked out of the window, what did she see but a great big Tiger tied up in front of their house, to the post to which they usually fastened the donkey; she was very much surprised, and running to her husband, awoke him, saying, 'Do you know what animal you fetched home last night?'

'Yes, the donkey, to be sure,' he answered.

'Come and see,' said she, and she showed him the great Tiger tied to the post. The Chattee-maker at this was no less astonished than his wife, and felt himself all over to find out if the Tiger had not wounded him. But no, there he was, safe and sound, and there was the Tiger tied to the post just as he had fastened it up the night before.

News of the Chattee-maker's exploit soon spread through the village, and all the people came to see him to hear him tell how he had caught the Tiger and tied it to the post. They thought that this was so wonderful that they sent a deputation to the Rajah with a letter to tell him how a man of their village had, alone and unarmed, caught a great Tiger, and he tied it to a post.

When the Rajah read the letter he also was much surprised and determined to go in person and see this astonishing sight. So he sent for his horses and carriages, his lords and attendants, and they all set off together to look at the Chattee-maker and the Tiger he had caught.

Now the Tiger was a very large one, and had long been the terror of all the country round, which made the whole matter still more extraordinary; and this being represented to the Rajah, he determined to confer every possible honour on the valiant Chattee-maker. So he gave him houses and lands, and as much money as would fill a well, made him lord of his court, and conferred on him the command of ten thousand horse.

It came to pass, shortly after this, that a neighbouring Rajah, who had long had a quarrel with this one, sent to announce his intention of going instantly to war with him; and tidings were at the same time brought that the Rajah who sent the challenge had gathered a great army together on the borders, and was prepared at a moment's notice to invade the country.

In this dilemma no one knew what to do. The Rajah sent for all his generals, and inquired which of them would be willing to take command of his forces and oppose the enemy. They all replied that the country was so ill-prepared for the emergency, and the case was apparently so hopeless, that they would rather not take the responsibility of the chief command. The Rajah knew not whom to appoint in their stead. Then some of his people said to him, 'You have lately given command of ten thousand horse to the valiant Chattee-maker who caught the Tiger, why not make him Commander-in-Chief? A man who could catch a Tiger and tie him to a post must surely be more courageous and clever than most. 'Very well,' said the Rajah, 'I will make him Commander-in-Chief.' So he sent for the Chattee-maker and said to him, 'In your hands I place all the power of the kingdom. So you must put our enemies to flight.' 'So be it,' answered the Chattee-maker, 'but, before I lead the whole army against the enemy, suffer me to go by myself and examine their position; and, if possible, find out their numbers and strength.'

The Rajah consented, and the Chattee-maker returned home to his wife, and said, 'They have made me Commander-in-Chief which is a very difficult post for me to fill because I shall have to ride at the head of all the army, and you know I never was on a horse in my life. But I have succeeded in gaining a little delay, as the Rajah has given me permission to go first alone, and reconnoitre the enemy's camp. Do you, therefore, provide a very quiet pony, for you know I cannot ride, and I will start tomorrow morning.'

But before the Chattee-maker had started, the Rajah sent over to him a most magnificent charger, richly caparisoned, which he begged he would ride when going to see the enemy's camp. The Chattee-maker was frightened almost out of his life, for the charger that the Rajah had sent him was very powerful and spirited. He felt sure that even if he ever got on it, he should very soon tumble off; however, he did not dare to refuse it, for fear of offending the Rajah by not accepting his present. So he sent him back a message of dutiful thanks, and said to his wife, 'I cannot go on the pony now that the Rajah has sent me this fine horse, but how am I ever to ride it?'

'Oh, don't be frightened,' she answered. 'You have only got to get upon it, and I will tie you firmly on so that you cannot tumble off, and if you start at night no one will see that you are tied on.'

'Very well,' he said. So that night his wife brought the horse that the Rajah had sent him to the door.

'Indeed,' said the Chattee-maker, 'I can never get into that saddle, it is so high up.'

'You must jump,' said his wife. Then he tried to jump several times, but each time he jumped, he tumbled down again.

'I always forget when I am jumping,' he said, 'which way I ought to turn.'

'Your face must be towards the horse's head,' she answered.

'To be sure, of course,' he cried, and giving one great jump, he jumped into the saddle, but with his face towards the horse's tail.

'This won't do at all,' said his wife as she helped him down again. 'Try getting on without jumping.'

'I never can remember,' he continued, 'when I have got my left foot in the stirrup, what to do with my right foot, or where to put it.'

'That must go in the other stirrup,' she answered. 'Let me help you.'

So, after many trials, in which he tumbled down very often, for the horse was fresh and did not like standing still, the Chattee-maker got into the saddle, but no sooner had he got there he cried, 'O wife, wife! tie me very firmly as quickly as possible, for I know I shall jump down if I can.' Then she fetched some strong rope and tied his feet firmly into the stirrups, fastened one stirrup to the other, put another rope round his waist, another round his neck, and fastened them to the horse's body, and neck, and tail.

When the horse felt all these ropes about him he could not imagine what queer creature had got upon his back, and he began rearing, and kicking, and prancing, and at last set off full gallop, as fast as he could tear, right across country. 'Wife, wife,' cried the Chattee-maker, 'you forgot to tie my hands.'

'Never mind,' said she, 'hold on by the mane.' So he caught hold of the horse's mane as firmly as he could. Then away the horse went, away went the Chattee-maker, away, away, away, over hedges, over ditches, over rivers, over plains, away, away, like a flash of lightning, now this way, now that, on, on, on, gallop, gallop, gallop, until they came in sight of the enemy's camp.

The Chattee-maker did not like his ride at all, and when he saw where it was leading him he liked it still less, for he thought the enemy would catch him and very likely kill him. So he determined to make one desperate effort to be free, he stretched out his hand as the horse shot past a young banyan-tree and seized hold of it with all his might hoping the resistance it offered might cause the ropes that tied him to break. But the horse was going at his utmost speed, and the soil in which the banyan-tree grew was loose. When the Chattee-maker caught hold of it and gave it such a violent pull, it came up by the roots, and on he rode as fast as before, with the tree in his hand.

All the soldiers in the camp saw him coming, and had heard that an army was to be sent against them and that the Chattee-maker was one of the vanguard. 'See,' cried they, 'here comes a man of gigantic stature on a mighty horse! He rides at full speed across the country, tearing up the very trees in his rage! He is one of the opposing force; the whole army must be close at hand. If they are such as he, we are all dead men.' Then, running to their Rajah, some of them cried again, 'Here comes the whole force of the enemy' (for the story had by this time become exaggerated). 'They are men of gigantic stature, mounted on mighty horses. As they come, they tear up the very trees in their rage; we can oppose men, but not monsters such as these.' These were followed by others, who said, 'It is all true,' for by this time the Chattee-maker had got pretty near the camp. 'They're coming! They're coming! Let us fly! Let us fly! Fly, fly for your lives!' The whole panic-stricken multitude fled from the camp (those who had seen no cause for alarm going because the others did, or because they did not care to stay by themselves) after having obliged their Rajah to write a letter to the one whose country he was about to invade, to say that he would not do so, and propose terms of peace, and to sign it, and seal it with his seal. Scarcely had all the people fled from the camp, when the horse on which the Chattee-maker was came galloping into it, and on his back rode the Chattee-maker, almost dead from fatigue, with the banyan-tree in his hand. Just as he reached the camp the ropes by which he was tied broke, and he fell to the ground. The horse stood still, too tired with its long run to go further. On recovering his senses, the Chattee-maker discovered, to his surprise, that the whole camp, full of rich arms, clothes, and trappings, was entirely deserted. In the principal tent, moreover, he found a letter addressed to his Rajah, announcing the retreat of the invading army, and proposing terms of peace.

So he took the letter, and returned home with it as fast as he could, leading his horse all the way, for he was afraid to mount him again. It did not take him long to reach his house by the direct road, for whilst riding he had gone a more circuitous journey than was necessary, and he got there just at nightfall. His wife ran out to meet him, overjoyed at his speedy return. As soon as he saw her, he said, 'Ah, wife, since I saw you last I've been all around the world, and had many wonderful and terrible adventures. But never mind that now, send this letter quickly to the Rajah by a messenger, and also the horse that he sent for me to ride. He will then see, by the horse looking so tired, what a long ride I've had, and if he is sent on beforehand, I shall not be obliged to ride him up to the palace door tomorrow morning as I otherwise should. That would be very tiresome, for most likely I should tumble off.' So his wife sent the horse, the letter to the Rajah, and a message that her husband would be at the palace early next morning as it was then late at night. The next day, he went down there as he had said he would, and when the people saw him coming, they said, 'This man is as modest as he is brave; after having put our enemies to flight, he walks quite simply to the door instead of riding here in state as any other man would.'

THE GOLDEN MOUNTAIN

(RUSSIAN)

Once upon a time, there was a merchant's son who squandered and wasted all his goods. To such a pass did come at last that he had nothing to eat. So he seized a spade, went out into the market-place, and began waiting to see if anyone would hire him as a labourer. And behold, the merchant who was 700 times richer than anyone else came along in his gilded coach. All the day labourers saw him, and the whole lot of them immediately scattered in every direction and hid themselves in corners. The merchant's son alone remained standing in the marketplace. 'Do you want work, young man?' said the merchant, 'then take hire from me.'

'Right willingly, there was no other reason that I came to the market-place.'

'And what wage do you require?'

'If you lay me down 100 roubles a day, that is a bargain.'

'That is somewhat dear!'

'If you think it dear, go and seek a cheaper article; but this I know, crowds of people were here just now, you came, and away they all bolted.'

'Well, agreed! Come to-morrow to the haven.'

The next day, early in the morning, our merchant's son came to the haven. The merchant, who was one in 700, had already been awaiting him some time. They went on board the ship and went to sea. They sailed and sailed. In the midst of the sea, an island appeared. On this island stood high mountains, and on the seashore, something was burning like fire. 'Can that which I see be fire?' said the merchant's son.

'Nay, that is my little golden castle.'

They drew near to the island, and went ashore. His wife and daughter came forth to meet the merchant, who was one in 700. The daughter was beautiful with a beauty that no man can imagine or devise and no tale can tell. As soon as they had greeted one another, they went on to the castle and took the new labourer along with them. They sat down at table, and they began to eat, drink, and be merry. 'A fig for today,' said the host, 'today we'll feast. Tomorrow we'll work.'

The merchant's son was a fair youth, strong and stately, of a ruddy countenance like milk and blood, and he fell in love with the lovely damsel. She went out into the next room. She called him secretly, and gave him a flint and steel. 'Take them,' said she, 'and if you should be in any need, use them.'

The next day, the merchant, who was one in 700, set out with his servant for the high golden mountain. They climbed and climbed, but they climbed not up to the top; they crawled and crawled, but they crawled not up to the top. 'Well,' said the merchant, 'let's have a drink first of all.' The merchant handed him a sleeping poison. The labourer drank and fell asleep. The merchant drew out his knife and killed his wretched nag which he had brought with him. He took out its entrails, put the young man into the horse's stomach and the spade in too. He then sewed up the wound and went and hid himself among the bushes. Suddenly there flew down a whole host of black iron-beaked ravens. They took up the carcass, carried it up into the mountain, and fell a-pecking it. They began eating up the horse, and soon pierced right down to the merchant's son. Then when he awoke, he beat off the black crows, looked hither and thither, and asked himself, 'Where am I?'

The merchant, who was one in 700, bawled up at him, 'On the golden mountain. Come, take your spade and dig gold.' So he dug and dug, throwing it all down below, and the merchant put it on wagons. By evening, he had filled nine wagons. 'That'll do,' cried the merchant, who was one in 700. 'Thanks for your labour. Adieu!'

'But how about me?'

'You may get on as best you can. Ninety-nine of your sort have perished on that mountain. You will just make up the hundred!' spoke the merchant and departed.

'What's to be done now?' thought the merchant's son. 'To get down from this mountain is quite impossible. I shall certainly starve to death.' So, there he stood on the mountain, and above him, wheeled the black iron-beaked crows. They plainly scented their prey. He began to think to himself how all this had come to pass, and then it occurred to him how the lovely damsel had taken him aside to give him the flint and steel, and said to him, 'Take it, and if you are in need, make use of it.'

'And look now, she did not say it in vain. Let us try it.' The merchant's son took out the flint and steel. He struck it once, and immediately two fair young heroes jumped out. 'What do you want? What do you want?'

'Take me from this mountain to the seashore.' No sooner than he had spoken, they took him under the arms and bore him carefully down from the mountain. The merchant's son walked about by the shore, and lo, a ship was sailing by the island. 'Hi, good ship-folk, take me with you!'

'Nay, brother, we cannot stop. Such a stoppage would lose us 100 knots.' The mariners passed by the island. Contrary winds began to blow, and a frightful hurricane arose. 'Alas! He is no simple man of our sort. We had better turn back and take him on board ship.' So they returned to the island, stopped by the shore, took up the merchant's son, and conveyed him to his native town.

A long time, and a little time passed by. Then the merchant's son took his spade and again went out into the marketplace to wait for someone to hire him. Again, the merchant, who was one in 700, passed by in his gilded carriage. The day-labourers saw him, and scattered in every direction and hid themselves in corners. The merchant's son was the sole solitary little one left. 'Will you take hire from me?' said the merchant, who was one in 700.

'Willingly; put down 200 roubles a day, and set me my work.'

'Rather dear, eh?'

'If you find it dear, go and seek cheaper labour. You saw how many people were here, and the moment you appeared, they all ran away.'

'Well, then, done; come tomorrow to the haven.'

The next morning they met at the haven, went on board the ship, and sailed to the island. There they ate and drank their fill one whole day, and the next day they got up and went towards the golden mountain. When they arrived there, the merchant, who was one in 700, pulled out his drinking glass. 'Come now, let us have a drink first,' he said.

'Stop, mine host! You, who are the chief, ought to drink the first. Let me treat you with mine own drink.' And the merchant's son, who had provided himself with sleeping poison, poured out a full mass of it and gave it to the merchant, who was one in

700. He drank it off and fell into a sound sleep. The merchant's son slaughtered the sorriest horse, disembowelled it, laid his host in the horse's belly, put the spade there too, sewed up the wound, and went and hid himself among the bushes. Instantly, the black iron-beaked crows flew down, took up the carcass, carried it to the mountain, and fell a-pecking at it. The merchant, who was one in 700, awoke and looked hither and thither. 'Where am I?' he asked.

'On the mountain,' bawled the merchant's son. 'Take your spade and dig gold; if you dig much, I will show you how to get off the mountain.'

The merchant, who was one in 700, took his spade and dug and dug. He dug up 20 wagon loads. 'Stop, that's enough now,' said the merchant's son. 'Thanks for your labour, and good-bye.'

'But, what about me?'

'You? Why, get off as best you can. Ninety-nine of your sort have perished on that mountain, you can make up the hundred.' So; the merchant's son took all the 20 wagons, went to the golden castle, married the lovely damsel, the daughter of the merchant who was one in 700, took possession of all her riches, and came to live in the capital with his whole family. But the merchant, who was one in 700, remained there on the mountain, and the black iron-beaked crows picked his bones.

THE CROW PERI

(PERSIAN)

There was once a youth named Hassan, who was so poor that he had scarcely rags to cover him, and he was often obliged to go hungry to bed.

One day Hassan went out to the forest beyond the city and set a snare, hoping to catch a bird or some small animal that would serve him for a meal. After setting it, he hid himself in the bushes nearby to wait. He had not been there long when he heard a loud flapping, and running out he saw that a large black crow was caught in the snare.

Hassan was greatly disappointed. He had hoped for something more worth eating than a crow. However, even that was better than nothing. He took the bird from the snare, and was about to wring its neck when it spoke to him in a human voice.

'Hassan, Hassan, do not kill me! Spare my life and I will make your fortune for you.'

Hassan was greatly surprised to hear the crow speak, but after a moment he swallowed his surprise and answered it.

'Make my fortune!' cried he. 'How can you make my fortune? – you, a crow? No, no, I am hungry, and the best fortune that can happen to me now is to have a full stomach!'

Again he was about to wring the bird's neck, but it called to him so piteously that he could not but pause.

'Hassan! Hassan! You do not know what you are doing. I am no common crow. Let me go now, and if you return to-morrow

THE CROW PERI

to this same spot you will find something in the snare that will be worth more to you than I can possibly be.'

'Very well,' said Hassan. 'I will let you go, but I do this through pity, and not because I believe in the least that you can better my fortunes.'

'That is well,' said the crow. 'You will see, however, that I will keep my promise. But before you let me go, pluck three feathers from my wings. If you are ever in trouble, blow one of these feathers into the air and call to me, and I will come and give you aid.'

Hassan did as the crow bade him. He plucked three feathers from its wings, but as he did so he could not keep from laughing.

'You may laugh,' said the crow, 'but you will soon find that my promises are not vain. To-morrow return to your snare, and you will find in it something that will be of value to you.'

It then spread its wings and flew away over the tree-tops, flapping heavily.

Hassan returned home, but the next day he came to the forest again. As he approached the spot where the snare was, he gave a cry of joy and wonder. Caught in it was the most beautiful bird he had ever seen or dreamed of. Its feathers were of pure silver, and over them played the most gorgeous colours, like the colours of a rainbow. Its eyes shone like diamonds, and its crest was tipped with jewels of seven different kinds.

'Such a bird as this is not to be eaten,' said Hassan to himself. 'It is a gift that is fit for the King. I will take it to the palace and present it to him, and he will be sure to reward me handsomely.' At the same time he could not help marvelling to think how truly the crow had spoken.

The youth hastened back to the city and borrowed a cage from a neighbour. Then he returned to the tree, and put the wonderful bird in the cage, and set out for the palace. He had thrown a piece of cloth over the cage, so as to hide the bird, but the light from it was so bright that it shone through, and set everyone to wondering what it could be that the ragged youth was carrying so carefully.

At the palace Hassan found that it was a difficult matter to see the King. At last, however, he was allowed to come before his presence, and at once he uncovered the cage so that the bird could be seen.

The King was filled with wonder at the sight. He had never seen such a bird before. He questioned Hassan and made him repeat again and again the story of how he had caught the bird, and exactly what it was that the crow had said to him.

'There is some magic in this,' said the King. 'I will keep the bird, and never before have I received a gift that pleased me so much. I will also prove to you that the crow spoke the truth, for, from now on, your fortune is made.'

The King then caused the youth to be clothed in magnificent garments, and he also gave him for his own a handsome house near to the palace, and slaves to serve him, and gold to spend. Every day he sent for Hassan to come to him, and because the youth was clever and handsome and adroit, he soon became the King's favourite above all others.

But success is sure to make enemies. The King's former favourite became very jealous of Hassan, and he began to scheme to destroy the youth, and win back the King's favour to himself. One day he went to the King and said, 'What a pity it is that such a wonderful bird as Hassan has brought you should be kept in a cage! What it should have is an ivory palace, in which you could visit it and sit at ease to watch it.'

'That is true,' answered the King, 'but I do not know how I could obtain such a palace. There is not enough ivory in all my kingdom to build such a thing.'

'It is plain enough,' answered Hassan's enemy, 'that Hassan is the favourite of some magic power. Ask him to build the palace, and if he refuses, threaten him with death. Then I am sure that in some way he will be able to provide it for you.'

This the enemy said, not because he at all believed it, but because he wished to destroy Hassan.

After spending a short time in thought, the King agreed to this plan. He sent for Hassan and said to him, 'I am, as you know, greatly delighted with the bird that you have given me, but now I wish for still another thing. I wish you to build an ivory palace in which the bird can live, and in which I can go to visit it.'

'Alas, your Majesty, how can I build such a place as that?' cried Hassan. 'I have nothing of my own, as you know, but only what you yourself have given me, and in all your kingdom there is not enough ivory to build a whole palace of it.'

'Nevertheless, you must provide it,' answered the King, 'and if you do not do so, your life shall answer for it.'

When Hassan heard these words, he was greatly troubled. He went out from the King's presence and returned home, and there he prepared to die, for he knew not where to find enough ivory to build one room, to say nothing of a whole palace.

Suddenly, in the midst of his despair, he remembered the three feathers that he had plucked from the crow's wing. He feared they were lost, but after some search he found them laid away in a corner with the rags he had once worn. He took them up, and blowing one of them into the air he called upon the crow to come and help him.

Almost at once he heard outside a heavy flapping of wings, and a large crow flew in through the window and lighted beside him.

'What do you wish?' asked the crow, 'and why have you called upon me? Are you in trouble?'

'Trouble enough,' answered Hassan, 'and trouble that may end in my losing my life.' He then told the crow what it was that the King had demanded of him, and that he did not see how it would be possible for him to carry it out.

'Do not despair over this,' answered the crow. 'It is not such a difficult matter as you seem to think. Ask the King to give you 40 cartloads of wine, with bullocks to pull them, and 40 slaves to drive the carts, and do you come away with me into the forest, and I may be able to get the ivory for you.'

The youth had little hope of this. Still, he asked the King for the things, as the crow had bade him, – 40 cartloads of wine, the bullocks, and the 40 slaves, and the King was not slow to give them to him. Then Hassan went away with them into the forest, and the crow flew before to show him in which direction to go. After they had journeyed a long distance, they came to a pool, and all round this pool were marks that showed that it was the drinking-place for a great herd of elephants. There had been a drought, however, and the water had almost dried up.

The crow bade Hassan fill the pool with the wine he had brought with him, and this he did. Then, by the crow's directions, Hassan hid himself and the carts and bullocks and slaves some little distance away.

Toward evening there was a great noise of trampling and trumpeting in the forest, and a huge herd of elephants came down to the pool to drink. They were very thirsty, for the supply of water had been low for some days. When they found the pool full to the brim, they trumpeted with joy and rushed to it to drink. They drank and drank, and presently they were all overcome with the wine and fell down and lay as though dead.

Then Hassan called to the 40 slaves, and they came and cut off all the elephants' tusks and loaded them upon the carts, and there were 40 cartloads.

Hassan and his slaves and carts left the forest before the elephants awoke, and by the next day they were back in the city again.

When the King saw the loads of ivory that Hassan had brought with him, he could not wonder enough.

Hassan's enemy was filled with rage and envy, but he dissembled. 'Did I not know it?' said he to the King. 'I tell you there is nothing in the world that Hassan cannot do if only he wishes to.'

The ivory palace was built, and every day the King went there to sit and watch the bird, and Hassan was more of a favourite with him than ever.

But one day Hassan's enemy thought of a new plot to destroy him. He went to the King and said, 'What a pity it is that such a beautiful bird as this should never make a sound. No doubt it could make the most ravishing music if it would but sing.'

'Yes, it is a pity,' answered the King, and at once he became dissatisfied.

'It must be that the bird misses its former owner,' said the enemy. 'If Hassan really wished to please you, he would find the former owner and bring him here, so that the bird might sing again.'

'Yes, that is true,' said the King, 'and I would greatly like to hear it sing.'

He then sent for Hassan and told him what he wished.

'But, your Majesty,' cried Hassan in despair, 'I do not know who was the owner of the bird, nor have I any means for finding out. As you know, I caught it in a snare far away from the city, and where there is no house within sight.'

Nevertheless the King was determined that Hassan must find the former owner of the bird and bring him to the palace. If he did not, his life should answer for it.

Hassan went out from the King's presence very sad. Then he bethought himself of the crow's feathers. He took one of the two that still remained, and blew it into the air, and called to the crow to come.

Almost at once the crow appeared and settled on the ground beside him.

'What is it that you wish now?' it asked. 'Are you again in trouble?'

'Yes, I am in trouble, and my trouble is very grievous.' Hassan then told the crow what it was that the King demanded of him.

'This is a more difficult matter than the former one,' answered the crow. 'Nevertheless, it may be managed. Ask the King to give you a vessel fitted out in the most complete and magnificent way. The sails must be of silk and the figurehead of gold. It must be painted and gilded within and without. There must be a dining-hall hung about with velvet curtains, and the dishes must be of solid gold. There must also be a bathroom with a marble bath-tub, and there must be damsels on the ship, dressed in shining colours, and with bracelets and anklets of gold set with precious stones.

Do this, and then, when the vessel is ready, I will instruct you further.'

Hassan did as the crow bade him. He went to the King and asked him for a vessel fitted out in exactly the manner the crow had described to him. This the King gave him.

When the vessel was finished, Hassan went on board, taking the crow with him. They sailed away and sailed away, and always the crow told Hassan in which direction to steer. After seven days and seven nights, they came within sight of an island. The island was very pleasant to look upon, for there were flowers and trees loaded with fruit, and shining domes and palaces.

'Look, Hassan,' said the crow. 'That is the place whither we are bound. Now listen attentively to what I tell you, for I can guide you no farther; I must leave you, but if you will follow out exactly all my directions, everything will go well with you. That island belongs to the Queen of the Peris. She is a very powerful fairy, and very beautiful. She is very curious as well. When she sees your vessel, she will be anxious to find out about it, whence it comes, and who is the owner. She will send her messengers to inquire about it. But you must answer no questions, and you must let no one but the Queen herself come on board. She will wish to go all over the vessel, and when she sees the bathroom she will admire it so much that she will wish to take a bath there. This you must agree to. Then, while she is bathing, you must sail away with her, for she is the owner of the Wonder Bird, and for her and her alone will it sing.'

Hassan promised to do exactly as the crow bade him in all things, and then it spread its wings and flew away and out of sight. Hassan ordered the captain to sail the vessel up close to the shore of the island, and there they dropped anchor.

Presently he could see that they had been observed from the island. People gathered on the shore, many of them magnificently dressed, and presently several boats put out and were rowed over to the ship's side. In them were messengers from the Queen.

These messengers questioned Hassan as to whence the vessel came and whose it was. But Hassan would answer none of these questions. Neither would he allow them to come on board to examine the vessel, though they greatly wished it, and it had been, indeed, their Queen's commands that they should do so.

'If the Queen wishes to know about the vessel, she must come herself,' said Hassan.

The messengers returned to shore very much dissatisfied. But presently another boat put forth from the shore, and in it was the Queen herself. She was rowed over to the ship's side, and she said to the youth that she would now come on board herself and bring her maidens with her.

She was so beautiful and so magnificent that Hassan scarcely knew how to refuse her. However, he remembered the crow's words, and was determined to obey them.

'Your majesty, if you will do me the honour to enter my ship, it and all that are in it are yours,' he said; 'but as to anyone's coming on board with you, that I cannot allow, for I was expressly forbidden to permit anyone but yourself to visit the ship.'

The Queen was very much offended by Hassan's words. Still, she was so very curious that she could not resist coming on board to see whether the ship was really as magnificent within as it seemed from the outside.

The youth showed her all over it, and she was filled with admiration at the beauty and completeness of its furnishing. When she entered the room where the marble bath was, she was particularly delighted, and after examining all the arrangements she signified to Hassan that she would like to bathe in the marble tub.

Hassan at once retired and sent the damsels he had brought with him to attend the Queen.

While she was bathing, the sails were set, and the ship sailed away from the island and back across the sea toward Hassan's own country.

When the Queen had finished bathing, and had returned to the deck, she was amazed to find the ship under way and the island already lost to view. She commanded Hassan to carry her back at once to her island, but this the youth would in nowise consent to do. He explained to the Queen why it was that he had carried her of – that it was to save his own life. He said that later on, if she wished, she might return to her own country, but first she must see whether the bird belonged to her, and whether it would sing for her. He also told her so many pleasant things about the King, his master, that the Queen became quite curious to see him.

'I make no doubt from what you tell me,' said she, 'that the bird is one that I lost some time ago. If it is, I shall be glad to make it sing for your master, but after that I must of course return home, and I shall take the bird with me.'

The youth doubted whether the King would agree to this, but he kept his thoughts to himself, and at last brought the Queen to the city and into the King's palace.

When the King saw the lady Hassan had brought with him, he was amazed at her beauty. He could think of nothing else. Even the bird was forgotten. He caused her to sit at his right hand and did all he could to entertain her.

The Queen was no less pleased with him, and some time was spent in talking pleasantly together.

'And now, your Majesty,' said the Queen at last, 'let us visit the ivory palace where the Wonder Bird is kept, and see whether it is mine, and if it is, I can promise you that it will immediately begin to sing, and that its voice is as beautiful as its plumage.'

The King at once arose, and together they went to the ivory palace. No sooner had the Queen crossed the threshold than the bird burst into song, and its song was so beautiful that all who heard it stood as though enchanted. They could not stir, nor scarcely breathe until the song was ended.

After the first day at the King's palace, the Queen spoke no more of returning to her own island. She had fallen deeply in love with the King, and he with her.

Before long they were married, and then Hassan became more of a favourite with them than ever. Wealth and honours were heaped upon him, and there was nothing that the King and Queen were not ready to do for him.

The former favourite was more filled with rage and envy than ever. He could scarcely eat or sleep, he was so envious.

Now after the King and Queen had been married for little more than a year the Queen fell ill, and her illness was so grievous that all the doctors in the kingdom could do nothing for her. At last it seemed as though she must surely die.

When this became known, Hassan's enemy went to the King and said, 'Your Majesty, I am but an ignorant man. I know you think nothing of me or my words, but is it not possible that there is some drug in the Queen's own country that might cure her? And if so, why should not Hassan be sent to fetch it for her? For he and he alone knows where her island lies.'

THE CROW PERI

This the enemy said because he hoped that if Hassan returned to the island the people there would either kill him or make a prisoner of him because he had carried off their Queen.

The King, however, never thought of that. He thought only of what might save the Queen's life. The advice he received seemed to him very wise. He at once sent for Hassan and told him what he wished him to do – that he was to return to the Queen's own country, and demand of her court physician some drug that would make her well.

Hassan thoroughly understood how dangerous this errand might prove. He knew, too, why his enemy had suggested it; that it was not through any love of the Queen, but from hatred of him.

However, he said nothing of this to the King. He only agreed to what his master wished and at once made ready to set out. First, however, he took out the third feather that the crow had given him, blew it into the air, and called the crow to come to him.

At once the crow appeared.

'What would you have of me now?' it asked of the youth. 'Has some new trouble come upon you?'

'That I do not know,' answered Hassan, 'but the King is sending me upon a mission that may, it seems to me, prove very dangerous.'

He then told the crow what it was that the King required of him.

The crow seemed greatly disturbed when it heard of the Queen's illness. 'You must go,' it said, 'and go at once. There is indeed a drug in the Queen's palace that will save her life if you can but fetch it in time. You will suffer no harm from the people in the palace. They will, indeed, give you the drug at once when they learn that the Queen is in need of it. But at the gateway of the palace there are two fierce lions. These would certainly tear you to pieces before ever you could enter, unless you had my help to depend on.'

The crow then bade the youth look carefully at its right wing. 'You will find there a single silver feather,' it said. 'Pluck it out and carry it with you. When the lions spring at you, you must at once touch them with that feather, and then they will become gentle, and you can pass them by unharmed.'

The crow stooped before Hassan and spread wide its wings, and Hassan saw that the third feather from the tip of the right wing was of pure silver. He plucked it out, and having hidden it in a safe place in his clothing, he started out on his journey. For seven days and seven nights he sailed across the seas in the same direction as he had gone before, and on the morning of the eighth day he came within sight of the island. He landed and made his way toward the palace, and he saw no one on his way. No sooner did he approach the gateway than two fierce lions sprang out and rushed at him as though to tear him to pieces.

Hassan was terrified at their appearance. It seemed as though he must surely lose his life, but he stood firm until they were almost upon him, and then he touched them with the feather. At once they became perfectly gentle, and even fawned at his feet as though he were their master. So Hassan passed by them unharmed and entered the palace.

Those who were there were very much surprised to see a stranger enter. They could not understand how it was he had been able to pass by the lions without being torn to pieces.

The youth explained the matter to them, however, and showed them the silver feather. He also told them the sore need of their

Queen, and begged them, if they had any drug that could save her, to bring it to him at once and let him go.

The people of the palace looked at him strangely when he showed them the feather. But when he made known the illness of the Queen they hastened to fetch a drug she always used, and gave it to him.

'This will save her,' they told him, 'for she has often used it to bring back life when it was almost gone.'

They then escorted him to the seashore, showing him the greatest honour, and many of them wished to return with him to the King's country, but this he dared not allow.

It was again seven days and seven nights before Hassan came to the end of the journey, and by that time the King was in despair. He had no longer any hope. However, when he heard that the ship had arrived, he sent his swiftest horses and riders to meet Hassan and bring him to the palace.

The youth was at once taken into the room where the Queen was lying stretched upon a couch, seemingly lifeless. The King, the court physician, and her attendants were with her.

'Have you brought it? The drug?' cried the King.

Hassan drew it forth from his bosom, where he carried it, and placed it in the hands of the Queen's physician. He did not notice that the crow had followed him into the room.

The physician poured a few drops of the drug into a goblet and held it to the Queen's lips. No sooner had she swallowed it than a wonderful change came over her. The colour returned to her cheeks and the life to her limbs. She opened her eyes and sat up and looked about her.

At once her eyes fell upon the crow, and it was to it that she addressed her first words.

'Oh, thou careless and disobedient one!' she cried, 'into what danger didst thou not throw thy mistress.'

'Alas!' answered the crow, 'thou hast indeed been near to death. But all that is over now. There is only happiness before thee. But for me, is my misery never to end?'

'Yes, and that right soon,' cried the Queen. 'If I owe my danger to thee, so also do I owe to thee my happiness. Draw near to me.'

All in the room had listened in wonder to this talk between the Queen and the crow. But a still stranger thing was to happen.

As the crow hopped close to the couch, the Queen took a few drops of water from a vial nearby and sprinkled it over the bird, at the same time pronouncing some magic words.

At once, instead of the crow, a tall and graceful maiden stood there before the Queen, a maiden of such great beauty that she was even the equal of the Queen herself.

The King and Hassan were filled with wonder at this sight.

The Queen then turned to the King with a gentle smile.

'This maiden,' said she, 'was my favourite of all the Peris that once attended me. But she grew proud and haughty because of my favour, and at last presumed to disobey even me. To punish her, I changed her into a crow and sent her to fly about the world, despised by all. But I will now forgive her because she brought me to you, and will take her back into favour if she can assure me of her repentance.'

The Peri sank on her knees before the Queen and kissed her hand, weeping. She assured her mistress that her pride was indeed broken, and that from now on she would be her faithful and obedient servant.

The Queen then raised her from her knees and made her sit beside her, and all was joy and happiness.

As for Hassan, he found the maiden so beautiful that he could not keep his eyes from her. Already he loved her with his whole heart, and longed for nothing so much as to have her for a wife. The Peri returned his love, and with the consent of the King and Queen they were married, and from that time on they lived in the greatest joy and contentment.

As for the former favourite, he was so miserable over the sight of Hassan's happiness that at length he could bear it no longer. He sold his house and goods and sailed away, no one knew whither, and if anyone regretted him, it was not Hassan.

THE BETROTHED OF DESTINY

(ARMENIAN)

Once upon a time the King of the West had a son who, one night, dreamed a dream in which destiny betrothed him to the daughter of the King of the East. In the morning he awoke, and lo! the betrothal ring of the maiden was on his finger. On the very same night the same dream had come to the sleeping maiden, who on the morrow found on her finger the betrothal ring of the son of the King of the West. The lad at once started to find his betrothed, and after a long journey came to the city of the King of the East. He entered into the service of the King as a stranger, because he could not make himself known on account of the continuous strife existing between his father and the King of the East. He served the King seven years, during which he spent many happy hours with the young princess, his betrothed. At the expiration of the seven years he asked the hand of the princess as a remuneration for his services. The King, who was pleased with the lad, consented to give him his daughter in marriage. But the lad said he must take her to his country, where the wedding should take place. The King consented to that also, and let his daughter go, giving her a precious dower. On their way to the country of the King of the West they had to cross the sea, and so went on board a ship. The captain, being a wicked man, was charmed by the beauty of the maiden, and before the ship sailed he sent the lad ashore, bidding him to make further preparation, as the voyage would probably be long on account of contrary winds. As soon as the lad disappeared the captain weighed anchor and set sail. The lad came back only to find that the ship had sailed away with his love on board. There remained nothing for him to do but to lament and bewail his ill luck. The maiden, who was in the cabin, did not discover the truth until it was too late. To her censure and upbraiding the vile captain answered with the proposal that she should become his wife.

'I marry you! such an ungracious beast as you!' she exclaimed. 'I would rather make my grave in the unfathomable sea.'

But the captain was strong, and they were on the open sea where no help could be expected. Seeing that she could not resist force if the captain resorted to it, she resolved to use craft.

'Well, then,' she answered finally, 'I will be your wife, but not upon the sea. We will go home to your city and there be married lawfully.'

The captain consented, and they soon reached the city.

'Now, do you go first,' said the maiden, 'and make preparation. I will wait here until you return.'

Without suspicion the captain went ashore. As soon as he had disappeared the maiden bade the sailors weigh anchor, and she set sail without knowing where to go. At last she reached a certain city and cast anchor. The King of that city was a young lad of marriageable age, who was celebrating his wedding festival. Thirty-nine beautiful maidens were already elected; only one maiden was missing to complete the number 40 from among whom he would choose his queen, while the others were to become handmaids to the queen-elect. The King, hearing that a beautiful maiden had come to the haven, hastened thither, and seeing the princess, said to her:

'Fair maiden, come and by your presence complete the number 40. You are the jewel of all the maidens, and will surely be my dear queen, while the rest shall become your handmaids.'

'Very well, I will come,' answered the princess; 'only send hither your 39 maidens, that I may come to your palace with great pomp.'

The youthful King consented and sent his maidens on board the ship. As soon as they came, the princess weighed anchor and set sail. She told the 39 maidens who she was, and asked them to accompany her until destiny showed them what to do. The maidens were fascinated by her beauty and commanding appearance, and promised to follow her wherever she went, even to the end of the earth. After sailing for a long time, they came to an unknown shore where there was a castle. They cast anchor and all the party landed. Entering the castle, they found in it 40 rooms with a bed in each, all richly decorated. The castle contained great wealth and abundant food. Satisfying their hunger, they went to bed, each maiden occupying a chamber. In the middle of the night the door of the castle suddenly opened, and there entered 40 brigands, who were the owners of the stronghold, and who were just returning from a nightly foray, bringing with them great booty.

'Aha!' exclaimed the brigands, seeing the maidens, 'we hunted elsewhere, and lo! the antelopes have come to our own home.'

'Enter, you brave heroes,' said the maidens; 'we were waiting for you.'

And they pretended to be very much pleased to see the brigands, who entered the rooms occupied by the maidens without suspicion. When they had laid down their arms and retired to rest, each maiden took the sword of the brigand who lay in her room and cut off his head. Thus the maidens were the owners of their wealth and property. In the morning the maidens rose, and putting on the clothes and arms of the robbers, appeared as youthful knights. They mounted the brigands' horses, taking in their saddlebags gold, silver, jewels and other portable wealth. After a long journey they came to the city of the King of the West, and encamped in a meadow on the outskirts of the city. Soon they heard a herald crying that on the following day there should be elected a King of the realm, for inasmuch as the late sovereign had died and the heir-apparent was lost, it was necessary to choose a new ruler. On the following day all the people of the realm were gathered in the park adjoining the palace; the 40 strangers also went to gratify their curiosity. Soon the nobles let loose the royal eagle, which flapped its wings and soared over the immense crowd, as though searching with its keen eyes for the true candidate for the throne. The multitude held their breath and stood stone-still. The royal bird once more flapped its wings, and descending from its towering flight, perched upon the head of the princess, who was disguised as a knight.

'That is a mistake,' exclaimed the noblemen; 'we must try it again.'

Once more they let loose the royal eagle, but again it alighted upon the head of the same stranger. A third trial gave the same result. Thereupon all the multitude saluted the disguised princess, the elect of destiny, exclaiming with one voice: 'Long live the King!' And with great pomp they took her and her companions to the royal palace, where the princess was anointed with holy oil, and crowned King over the realm, and her companions were made ministers.

This new King proved to be the wisest and most just ruler that that country had ever enjoyed, and all the people of the realm loved and honoured their sovereign with all their hearts. She built a splendid fountain in the midst of the city, on which she caused her image to be carved, so that everyone who came to drink might see it. She put guards to watch the fountain day and night, and said to them:

'Watch carefully, and when you perceive a stranger who, on seeing my image, shows signs of knowing me, bring him hither.'

One day there came a stranger who, after drinking, raised his eyes and saw the image. He gazed for a long time, and sighed deeply. Immediately he was arrested and taken to the King, who, looking at him from behind a curtain, ordered him to be imprisoned. This was the captain of the ship. On another day there came another stranger, and he also sighed. It was the King, the owner of the 39 maidens. He was kept in an apartment of the palace. And at last, disguised as a stranger, came the Prince, the betrothed of the ruling sovereign, and the heir-apparent to the crown. He also looked at the image and sighed, and was taken to the palace. Thereupon the princess summoned a parliament of all the nobility and the learned and wise men of the realm. She caused the three strangers to be brought before the assembly, and told her story from beginning to end.

The captain was condemned to be hanged, and was executed forthwith. The lord of the 39 maidens received them all, to whose number the princess added one of her most beautiful handmaids, thus making up the 40. The prince and the princess, the betrothed of destiny, celebrated their wedding with great joy and pomp for 40 days and 40 nights. The prince, as the true heir, was crowned King, his consort became Queen, and they reigned together.

Thus they reached their desire. May all of us attain our desires and the happiness ordained to us by an all-wise Providence.

Three apples fell from Heaven; one for me, one for the storyteller, and one for him who entertained the company.

THE PALACE OF EAGLES

(JEWISH)

East of the Land of the Rising Sun, there dwelled a king who spent all his days and half his nights in pleasure. His kingdom was on the edge of the world, according to the knowledge of those times, and almost entirely surrounded by the sea. Nobody seemed to care what lay beyond the barrier of rocks that shut off the land from the rest of the world. For the matter of that, nobody appeared to trouble much about anything in that kingdom. Most of the people followed the example of the king and led idle, careless lives, giving no thought to the future. The king regarded the task of governing his subjects as a big nuisance; he did not care to be worried with proposals concerning the welfare of the masses, and documents brought to him by his advisors for signature were never read. For he knew they may have referred to the school regulations of the moon, instead of the laws of trading and such like public matter.

'Don't bother me,' was his usual remark. 'You are my advisors and officers of state. Deal with affairs as you think best.'

And off he would go to his beloved hunting which was his favourite pastime.

The land was fertile, and nobody had ever entertained an idea that bad weather might some year affect the crops and cause a scarcity of grain. They took no precautions to lay in stocks of wheat, and so when one summer there was a great lack of rain and the fields were parched, the winter that followed was marked by suffering. The kingdom was faced by famine, and the people did not like it. They did not know what to do, and when they appealed to the king, he could not help them. Indeed, he could not understand the difficulty. He passed it off very lightly.

'I am a mighty hunter,' he said. 'I can always kill enough beasts to provide a sufficiency of food.'

But the drought had withered away the grass and the trees, and the shortage of such food had greatly reduced the number of animals. The king found the forests empty of deer and birds. Still he failed to realize the gravity of the situation and what he considered an exceedingly bright idea struck him.

'I will explore the unknown territory beyond the barrier of rocky hills,' he said. 'Surely there will I find a land of plenty. At least,' he added, 'it will be a pleasant adventure with good hunting.'

A great expedition was therefore arranged, and the king and his hunting companions set forth to find a path over the rocks. This was not at all difficult, and on the third day, a pass was discovered among the crags and peaks that formed the summit of the barrier, and the king saw the region beyond.

It seemed a vast and beautiful land, stretching away as far as the eye could see in a forest of huge trees. Carefully, the hunters descended the other side of the rock barrier and entered the unknown land.

It seemed uninhabited. Nor was there any sign of beast or bird of any kind. No sound disturbed the stillness of the forest, no tracks were visible. As well as the hunters could make out, no foot had ever trodden the region before. Even nature seemed at rest. The trees were all old, their trunks gnarled into fantastic shapes, their leaves yellow and sere as if growth had stopped ages ago.

Altogether the march through the forest was rather eerie, and the hunters proceeded in single file, which added to the impressiveness of the strange experience. The novelty, however, made it pleasant to the king, and he kept on his way for four days. Then the forest ended abruptly, and the explorers came to a vast open plain, a desert, through which a wide river flowed. Far beyond rose a mountain capped by rocks of regular shape. At any rate, they appeared to be rocks, but the distance was too great to enable anyone to speak with certainty.

'Water,' said the vizier, 'is a sign of life.'

So the king decided to continue as far as the mountain. A ford was discovered in the river, and once on the other side it was possible to make out the rocks crowning the mountain. They looked too regular to be mere rocks, and on approaching nearer the king was sure that a huge building must be at the top of the mountain. When they arrived quite close, there was no doubt about it. Either a town, or a palace, stood on the summit, and it was decided to make the ascent next day.

During the night no sound was heard, but to everybody's surprise a distinct path up the mountain was noticed in the morning. It was so overgrown with weeds and moss and straggling creepers that it was obvious it had not been used for a long time. The ascent was accordingly difficult, but halfway up the first sign of life, noticed since the expedition began, made itself visible. It was an eagle. Suddenly it flew down from the mountain top and circled above the hunters, screaming, but making no attempt to attack. At length the summit was gained. It was a flat plateau of great expanse, almost the whole of which was covered by an enormous building of massive walls and stupendous towers.

'This is the palace of a great monarch,' said the king.

But no entrance of any kind could be seen. The rest of the day was spent in wandering around, but nowhere was a door, or window, or opening visible. It was decided to make a more serious effort next morning to gain entry. However, it seemed a greater puzzle than ever. At length, one of the most venturesome of the party discovered an eagle's nest on one of the smallest towers, and with great difficulty, he secured the bird and brought it down to the king. His majesty bade one of his wise men, Muflog, learned in bird languages, to speak to it. He did so.

In a harsh croaking voice, the eagle replied, 'I am but a young bird, only seven centuries old. I know nothing. On a tower higher than that on which I dwell, is the eyrie of my father. He may be able to give you information.'

More he would not say. The only thing to do was to climb the higher tower and question the father eagle. This was done, and the bird answered, 'On a tower still higher dwells my father, and on yet a higher tower my grandfather, who is 2,000 years old. He may know something. I know nothing.'

After considerable difficulty the topmost tower was reached and the venerable bird discovered. He seemed asleep and was only awakened after much coaxing. Then he surveyed the hunters warily.

'Let me see, let me think,' he muttered slowly. 'I did hear, when I was a tiny eagle chick, but a few years old – that was a long, long ago – that my great-grandfather had said that his great-grandfather had told him he had heard that long, long, long ago – oh, ever so much longer than that – a king lived in this palace. He died and left it to the eagles, and that in the course of many, many, many thousands of years the door had been covered up by the dust brought by the winds.'

'Where is the door?' asked Muflog.

That was a puzzle the ancient bird could not answer readily. He thought and thought and fell asleep and had to be kept being awakened until at last, he remembered.

'When the sun shines in the morning,' he croaked, 'its first ray falls on the door.'

Then, worn out with all his thinking and talking, he fell asleep again.

There was no rest for the party that night. They all watched to make certain of seeing the first ray of the rising sun strike the palace. When it did so, the spot was carefully noted. But no door could be seen. Digging was therefore begun and after many hours, an opening was found.

Through this an entrance was effected into the palace. What a wonderful and mysterious place it was, all overgrown with the weeds of centuries! Tangled masses of creepers lay everywhere – over what were once trimly kept pathways, and almost completely hiding the lower buildings. In the crevices of the walls, roots had insinuated themselves, and by their growth had forced the stones apart. It was all a terrible scene of desolation. The king's men had to hack away laboriously through the wilderness of weeds with their swords to the central building, and when they did so they came to a door on which was an inscription cut deep into the wood. The language was unknown to all but Muflog, who deciphered it as follows:

'We, the Dwellers in this Palace, lived for many years in Comfort and Luxury. Then Hunger came. We had made no preparation. We had amassed jewels in abundance but not Corn. We ground Pearls and Rubies to fine flour, but could make no Bread. Wherefore we die, bequeathing this Palace to the eagles who will devour our bodies and build their eyries on our towers.'

A dread silence fell on the whole party when Muflog read these strange words, and the king turned pale. This warning from the dead past was making the adventure far from enjoyable. Some of the party suggested the immediate abandonment of the expedition and the prompt return to home. They feared hidden dangers now. But the king remained resolute.

'I must investigate this to the end,' he said in a firm voice. 'Those who are seized by fear may return. I will go on, if needs be, alone.'

Encouraged by these words, the hunters decided to remain with the king. One of them began to batter at the door, but the king was anxious to preserve the inscription, and after more cutting away of weeds, the key was seen to be sticking in the keyhole. Unlocking the door, however, was no light task, for ages of rust had accumulated. When finally this was accomplished the door creaked heavily on its hinges and a musty smell came from the dank corridor that was revealed.

The explorers walked ankle-deep in dust through a maze of rooms until they came to a big central hall of statues. So artistically fashioned were they that they seemed lifelike in their attitudes, and for a moment all held their breath. This hall was dustless, and Muflog pointed out that it was an airtight chamber. Evidently it had been specifically devised to preserve the statues.

'These must be the effigies of kings,' said his majesty, and on reading the inscriptions, Muflog said that was so.

At the far end of the hall, on a pedestal higher than the others, was a statue bigger than the rest. In addition to the name there was an inscription on the pedestal. Muflog read it amid an awed stillness, 'I am the last of the kings – yea, the last of men, and with my own hands have completed this work. I ruled over a thousand cities, rode on a thousand horses, and received the homage of a thousand vassal princes; but when Famine came I was powerless. Ye who may read this, take heed of the fate that has overwhelmed this land. Take but one word of counsel from the last of the mortals; prepare thy meal while the daylight lasts.'

The words broke off: the rest was undecipherable.

'Enough,' cried the king, and his voice was not steady. 'This has indeed been good hunting. I have learned, in my folly and pursuit of pleasure, what I had failed to see for myself. Let us return and act upon the counsel of this king who has met the end that will surely be our own should we forget his warning.'

Looking out across the plain they had traversed, his majesty seemed to see a vision of prosperous cities and smiling fertile fields. In imagination, he saw caravans laden with merchandise journeying across the intervening spaces. Then, as darker thoughts followed, a cloud appeared to settle over the whole land. The cities crumbled and disappeared, the eagles swooped down and took possession of that which man had failed to appreciate and hold. After the eagles, the dust of the ages settled slowly, piling itself up year by year until everything was covered and only the desert was visible. Scarcely a word was spoken as the king and his hunters made their way back to the land East of the Rising Sun. In all, they had been away 40 days when they re-crossed the barrier of rocks. They were joyously welcomed.

'What have you brought?' asked the populace. 'In a little while we shall be starving.'

'Ye shall not starve,' said the king. 'I have brought wisdom from the Palace of the Eagles. From the fate and sufferings of others I have learned a lesson – my duty.'

At once he set to work to organize the proper distribution of the food supply and the cultivation of the land. He wasted no more time on foolish pleasures, and in due course the land East of the Rising Sun enjoyed happiness and prosperity and even established fruitful colonies in the plain overlooked by the Palace of the Eagles.

FORTUNATUS AND HIS PURSE

(CYPRIOT)

Once upon a time there lived in the city of Famagosta, in the island of Cyprus, a rich man called Theodorus. He ought to have been the happiest person in the whole world, as he had all he could wish for, and a wife and little son whom he loved dearly; but unluckily, after a short time he always grew tired of everything, and had to seek new pleasures. When people are made like this the end is generally the same, and before Fortunatus (for that was the boy's name) was ten years old, his father had spent all his money and had not a farthing left.

But though Theodorus had been so foolish he was not quite without sense, and set about getting work at once. His wife, too, instead of reproaching him, sent away the servants and sold their fine horses, and did all the work of the house herself, even washing the clothes of her husband and child.

Thus time passed till Fortunatus was 16. One day when they were sitting at supper, the boy said to Theodorus, 'Father, why do you look so sad? Tell me what is wrong, and perhaps I can help you.'

'Ah, my son, I have reason enough to be sad; but for me you would now have been enjoying every kind of pleasure, instead of being buried in this tiny house.'

'Oh, do not let that trouble you,' replied Fortunatus, 'it is time I made some money for myself. To be sure I have never been taught any trade. Still there must be something I can do. I will go and walk on the seashore and think about it.'

Very soon – sooner than he expected – a chance came, and Fortunatus, like a wise boy, seized on it at once. The post offered him was that of page to the Earl of Flanders, and as the Earl's daughter was just going to be married, splendid festivities were held in her honour, and at some of the tilting matches Fortunatus was lucky enough to win the prize. These prizes, together with presents from the lords and ladies of the court, who liked him for his pleasant ways, made Fortunatus feel quite a rich man.

But though his head was not turned by the notice taken of him, it excited the envy of some of the other pages about the court, and one of them, called Robert, invented a plot to move Fortunatus out of his way. So he told the young man that the Earl had taken a dislike to him and meant to kill him; Fortunatus believed the story, and packing up his fine clothes and money, slipped away before dawn.

He went to a great many big towns and lived well, and as he was generous and not wiser than most youths of his age, he very soon found himself penniless. Like his father, he then began to think of work, and tramped half over Brittany in search of it. Nobody seemed to want him, and he wandered about from one place to another, till he found himself in a dense wood, without any paths, and not much light. Here he spent two whole days, with nothing to eat and very little water to drink, going first in one direction and then in another, but never being able to find his way out. During the first night he slept soundly, and was too tired to fear either man or beast, but when darkness came on for the second time, and growls were heard in the distance, he grew frightened and looked about for a high tree out of reach of his enemies. Hardly had he settled himself comfortably in one of the forked branches, when a lion walked up to a spring that burst from a rock close to the tree, and crouching down drank greedily. This was bad enough, but after all, lions do not climb trees, and as long as Fortunatus stayed up on his perch, he was quite safe. But no sooner was the lion out of sight, than his place was taken by a bear, and bears, as Fortunatus knew very well, *are* tree-climbers. His heart beat fast, and not without reason, for as the bear turned away he looked up and saw Fortunatus!

Now in those days every young man carried a sword slung to his belt, and it was a fashion that came in very handily for Fortunatus. He drew his sword, and when the bear got within a yard of him he made a fierce lunge forward. The bear, wild with pain, tried to spring, but the bough he was standing on broke with his weight, and he fell heavily to the ground. Then Fortunatus descended from his tree (first taking good care to see no other wild animals were in sight) and killed him with a single blow. He was just thinking he would light a fire and make a hearty dinner of bear's flesh, which is not at all bad eating, when he beheld a beautiful lady standing by his side leaning on a wheel, and her eyes hidden by a bandage.

'I am Dame Fortune,' she said, 'and I have a gift for you. Shall it be wisdom, strength, long life, riches, health, or beauty? Think well, and tell me what you will have.'

But Fortunatus, who had proved the truth of the proverb that 'It's ill thinking on an empty stomach,' answered quickly, 'Good lady, let me have riches in such plenty that I may never again be as hungry as I am now.'

And the lady held out a purse and told him he had only to put his hand into it, and he and his children would always find ten pieces of gold. But when they were dead it would be a magic purse no longer.

At this news Fortunatus was beside himself with joy, and could hardly find words to thank the lady. But she told him that the best thing he could do was to find his way out of the wood, and before bidding him farewell pointed out which path he should take. He walked along it as fast as his weakness would let him, until a welcome light at a little distance showed him that a house was near. It turned out to be an inn, but before entering Fortunatus thought he had better make sure of the truth of what the lady had told him, and took out the purse and looked inside. Sure enough there were the ten pieces of gold, shining brightly. Then Fortunatus walked boldly up to the inn, and ordered them to get ready a good supper at once, as he was very hungry, and to bring him the best wine in the house. And he seemed to care so little what he spent that everybody thought he was a great lord, and vied with each other who should run quickest when he called.

After a night passed in a soft bed, Fortunatus felt so much better that he asked the landlord if he could find him some men-servants, and tell him where any good horses were to be got. The next thing was to provide himself with smart clothes, and then to take a big house where he could give great feasts to the nobles and beautiful ladies who lived in palaces round about.

In this manner a whole year soon slipped away, and Fortunatus was so busy amusing himself that he never once remembered his parents whom he had left behind in Cyprus. But though he was thoughtless, he was not bad-hearted. As soon as their existence crossed his mind, he set about making preparations to visit them, and as he was not fond of being alone he looked round for someone older and wiser than himself to travel with him. It was not long before he had the good luck to come across an old man who had left his wife and children in a far country many years before, when he went out into the world to seek the fortune which he never found. He agreed to accompany Fortunatus back to Cyprus, but only on condition he should first be allowed to return for a few weeks to his own home before venturing to set sail for an island so strange and distant. Fortunatus agreed to his proposal, and as he was always fond of anything new, said that he would go with him.

The journey was long, and they had to cross many large rivers, and climb over high mountains, and find their way through thick woods, before they reached at length the old man's castle. His wife and children had almost given up hopes of seeing him again, and crowded eagerly round him. Indeed, it did not take Fortunatus five minutes to fall in love with the youngest daughter, the most beautiful creature in the whole world, whose name was Cassandra.

'Give her to me for my wife,' he said to the old man, 'and let us all go together to Famagosta.'

So a ship was bought big enough to hold Fortunatus, the old man and his wife, and their ten children – five of them sons and five daughters. And the day before they sailed the wedding was celebrated with magnificent rejoicings, and everybody thought that Fortunatus must certainly be a prince in disguise. But when they reached Cyprus, he learned to his sorrow that both his father and mother were dead, and for some time he shut himself up in his house and would see nobody, full of shame at having forgotten them all these years. Then he begged that the old man and his wife would remain with him, and take the place of his parents.

For twelve years Fortunatus and Cassandra and their two little boys lived happily in Famagosta. They had a beautiful house and everything they could possibly want, and when Cassandra's sisters married the purse provided them each with a fortune. But at last Fortunatus grew tired of staying at home, and thought he should like to go out and see the world again. Cassandra shed many tears at first when he told her of his wishes, and he had a great deal of trouble to persuade her to give her consent. But on his promising to return at the end of two years she agreed to let him go. Before he went away he showed her three chests of gold, which stood in a room with an iron door, and walls 12 feet thick. 'If anything should happen to me,' he said, 'and I should never come back, keep one of the chests for yourself, and give the others to our two sons.' Then he embraced them all and took a ship for Alexandria.

The wind was fair and in a few days they entered the harbour, where Fortunatus was informed by a man whom he met on landing, that if he wished to be well received in the town, he must begin by making a handsome present to the Sultan. 'That is easily done,' said Fortunatus, and went into a goldsmith's shop, where he bought a large gold cup, which cost 5,000 pounds. This gift so pleased the Sultan that he ordered 100 casks of spices to be given to Fortunatus; Fortunatus put them on board his ship, and commanded the captain to return to Cyprus and deliver them to his wife, Cassandra. He next obtained an audience of the Sultan, and begged permission to travel through the country, which the Sultan readily gave him, adding some letters to the rulers of other lands which Fortunatus might wish to visit.

Filled with delight at feeling himself free to roam through the world once more, Fortunatus set out on his journey without losing a day. From court to court he went, astonishing everyone by the magnificence of his dress and the splendour of his presents. At length he grew as tired of wandering as he had been of staying at home, and returned to Alexandria, where he found the same ship that had brought him from Cyprus lying in the harbour. Of course the first thing he did was to pay his respects to the Sultan, who was eager to hear about his adventures.

When Fortunatus had told them all, the Sultan observed: 'Well, you have seen many wonderful things, but I have something to show you more wonderful still;' and he led him into a room where precious stones lay heaped against the walls. Fortunatus' eyes were quite dazzled, but the Sultan went on without pausing and opened a door at the farther end. As far as Fortunatus could see, the cupboard was quite bare, except for a little red cap, such as soldiers wear in Turkey.

'Look at this,' said the Sultan.

'But there is nothing very valuable about it,' answered Fortunatus. 'I've seen a dozen better caps than that, this very day.'

'Ah,' said the Sultan, 'you do not know what you are talking about. Whoever puts this cap on his head and wishes himself in any place, will find himself there in a moment.'

'But who made it?' asked Fortunatus.

'That I cannot tell you,' replied the Sultan.

'Is it very heavy to wear?' asked Fortunatus.

'No, quite light,' replied the Sultan, 'just feel it.'

Fortunatus took the cap and put it on his head, and then, without thinking, wished himself back in the ship that was starting for Famagosta. In a second he was standing at the prow, while the anchor was being weighed, and while the Sultan was repenting of his folly in allowing Fortunatus to try on the cap, the vessel was making fast for Cyprus.

When it arrived, Fortunatus found his wife and children well, but the two old people were dead and buried. His sons had grown tall and strong, but unlike their father had no wish to see the world, and found their chief pleasure in hunting and tilting. In the main, Fortunatus was content to stay quietly at home, and if a restless fit did seize upon him, he was able to go away for a few hours without being missed, thanks to the cap, which he never sent back to the Sultan.

By-and-by he grew old, and feeling that he had not many days to live, he sent for his two sons, and showing them the purse and cap, he said to them: 'Never part with these precious possessions. They are worth more than all the gold and lands I leave behind me. But never tell their secret, even to your wife or dearest friend. That purse has served me well for 40 years, and no one knows whence I got my riches.' Then he died and was buried by his wife Cassandra, and he was mourned in Famagosta for many years.

THE SPEAKING GRAPES, THE SMILING APPLE AND THE TINKLING APRICOT

(MAGYAR)

There was once, I don't know where, beyond seven times and seven countries, a king who had three daughters.

One day the king was going to the market, and thus inquired of his daughters, 'What shall I bring you from the market, my dear daughters?' The eldest said, 'A golden dress, my dear royal father.' The second said, 'A silver dress for me.' The third said, 'Speaking grapes, a smiling apple, and a tinkling apricot for me.' 'Very well, my daughters,' said the king, and went. He bought the dresses for his two elder daughters in the market, as soon as he arrived, but, in spite of all exertions and inquiries, he could not find the speaking grapes, the smiling apple, and the tinkling apricot. He was very sad that he could not get what his youngest daughter wished for she was his favourite, and he went home. It happened, however, that the royal carriage stuck fast on the way home. Although his horses were of the best breed, they were such high steppers that they kicked the stars. So he at once sent for extra horses to drag out the carriage, but all in vain, the horses couldn't move either way. He gave up all hope, at last, of getting out of the position when a dirty, filthy pig came that way, and grunted:

'Grumph! Grumph! Grumph! King, give me your youngest daughter, and I will help you out of the mud.' The king, never thinking what he was promising and over-anxious to get away, consented, and the pig gave the carriage a push with its nose so that carriage and horses at once moved out of the mud. Having arrived at home, the king handed the dresses to his two daughters, and was now sadder than ever that he had brought nothing for his favourite daughter. The thought also troubled him that he had promised her to an unclean animal.

After a short time the pig arrived in the courtyard of the palace dragging a wheelbarrow after it, and grunted, 'Grumph! Grumph! Grumph! King, I've come for your daughter.' The king was terrified, and, in order to save his daughter, he had a peasant girl dressed in rich garments, embroidered with gold, sent her down and had her seated in the wheelbarrow. The pig again grunted, 'Grumph! Grumph! Grumph! King, this is not your daughter.' He took the wheelbarrow and tipped her out. The king, seeing that deceit was of no avail, sent down his daughter, as promised, but dressed in ragged, dirty tatters, thinking that she would not please the pig. But the animal grunted in great joy, seized the girl, and placed her in the wheelbarrow. Her father wept that, through a careless promise, he had brought his favourite daughter to such a fate. The pig went on and on with the sobbing girl, till, after a long journey, it stopped before a dirty pig sty and grunted, 'Grumph! Grumph! Grumph! Girl, get out of the wheelbarrow.' The girl did as she was told. 'Grumph! Grumph! Grumph!' grunted the pig again. 'Go into your new home.' The girl, whose tears, now, were streaming like a brook, obeyed. The pig then offered her some Indian corn that it had in a trough, and also its litter which consisted of some old straw, for a resting-place. The girl had not a wink of sleep for a long time, till at last, quite worn out with mental torture, she fell asleep.

Being completely exhausted with all her trials, she slept so soundly that she did not wake till next day at noon. On awaking, she looked round, and was very much astonished to find herself in a beautiful fairy-like palace, her bed being of white silk with rich purple curtains and golden fringes. At the first sign of her, waking maids appeared all round her, awaiting her orders, and bringing her costly dresses. The girl, quite enchanted with the scene, dressed without a word, and the maids accompanied her to her breakfast in a splendid hall where a young man received her with great affection. 'I am your husband, if you accept me, and whatever you see here belongs to you,' he said. After breakfast, he led her into a beautiful garden. The girl did not know whether it was a dream, or reality, and the young man gave evasive and chaffing replies to her questions. At this moment they came to that part of the garden which was laid out as an orchard, and the bunches of grapes began to speak, 'Our beautiful queen, pluck some of us.' The apples smiled at her continuously, and the apricots tinkled a beautiful silvery tune. 'You see, my love,' said the handsome youth, 'Here you have what you wished for which your father could not obtain. You may know now, that I was once a monarch, but I was bewitched into a pig. I had to remain in that state till a girl wished for speaking grapes, a smiling apple, and a tinkling apricot. You are the girl, and I have been delivered. If I please you, you can be mine for ever.' The girl was enchanted with the handsome youth and the royal splendour, and she consented. They went with great joy to carry the news to her father and to tell him of their happiness.

THE GOOD FERRYMAN CAPTURES THE MERMAID

(POLISH)

There was once an old man, very poor, with three sons. They lived chiefly by ferrying people over a river; but he had had nothing but ill-luck all his life. And to crown all, on the night he died, there was a great storm and the crazy old ferry-boat on which his sons depended for a living, was sunk.

As they were lamenting both their father and their poverty, an old man came by, and learning the reason of their sorrow, said:

'Never mind, all will come right in time. Look! There is your boat as good as new.'

And there was a fine new ferry-boat on the water in place of the old one, and a number of people waiting to be ferried over.

The three brothers arranged to take turns with the boat and divide the fares they took.

They were, however, very different in disposition. The two elder brothers were greedy and avaricious, and they would never take anyone over the river without being handsomely paid for it.

But the youngest brother took over poor people, who had no money, for nothing; and moreover frequently relieved their wants out of his own pocket.

One day, at sunset, when the eldest brother was at the ferry, the same old man who had visited them on the night their father died came and asked for a passage.

'I have nothing to pay you with but this empty purse,' he said.

'Go and get something to put in it then first,' replied the ferryman, 'and be off with you now!'

Next day it was the second brother's turn; the same old man came, and offered his empty purse as his fare. But he met with a like reply.

The third day it was the youngest brother's turn; when the old man arrived and asked to be ferried over for charity, he answered:

'Yes, get in, old man.'

'And what is the fare?' asked the old man.

'That depends upon whether you can pay or not,' was the reply. 'But if you cannot, it is all the same to me.'

'A good deed is never without its reward,' said the old man, 'but in the meantime take this empty purse though it is very worn and looks worth nothing. But if you shake it, and say, "For his sake who gave it, this purse I hold, I wish may always be full of gold," it will always afford you as much gold as you wish for.'

The youngest brother came home, and his brothers, who were sitting over a good supper, laughed at him because he had taken only a few copper coins that day, and they told him he should have no supper. But when he began to shake his purse and scatter gold coins all about, they jumped up from the table and began picking them up eagerly.

And as it was share and share alike, they all grew rich very quickly. The youngest brother made good use of his riches, for he gave away money freely to the poor. But the greedy elder brothers envied the possession of the wonderful purse, and they contrived to steal it from him. Then they left their old home and the one bought a ship, laden with all sorts of merchandise, for a trading voyage. But the ship ran upon a rock, and everyone on board drowned. The second brother was no more fortunate, for as he was travelling through a forest with an enormous treasure of precious stones in which he had laid out his wealth to sell at a profit, he was waylaid by robbers, who murdered him, and shared the spoil among them.

The youngest brother, who remained at home, having lost his purse became as poor as before. But he still did as formerly, took pay from passengers who could afford it, ferried over poor folks for nothing, and helped those who were poorer than himself so far as he could.

One day the same old man with the long white beard came by; the ferryman welcomed him as an old friend, and while rowing him over the river, told him all that had happened since he last saw him.

'Your brothers did very wrong, and they have paid for it,' said the old man; but you were in fault yourself. Still, I will give you one more chance. Take this hook and line and whatever you catch, mind you hold fast, and not let it escape you, or you will bitterly repent it.'

The old man then disappeared, and the ferryman looked in wonder at his new fishing-tackle: a diamond hook, a silver line, and a golden rod.

All at once the hook sprang of itself into the water. The line lengthened out along the river current, and there came a strong pull upon it. The fisherman drew it in, and beheld a most lovely creature, upwards from the waist a woman but with a fish's tail.

'Good ferryman, let me go,' she said. 'Take your hook out of my hair! The sun is setting, and after sunset I can no longer be a water-nymph again.'

But without answering, the ferryman only held her fast and covered her over with his coat to prevent her escaping. Then the sun set, and she lost her fish-tail.

'Now,' she said, 'I am yours; so let us go to the nearest church and get married.'

She was already dressed as a bride, with a myrtle garland on her head, in a white dress, with a rainbow-coloured girdle, and rich jewels in her hair and on her neck. In her hand she held the wonderful purse that was always full of gold.

They found the priest and all ready at the church. They were married in a few minutes, and then came home to their wedding-feast to which all the neighbours were invited. They were royally entertained and when they were about to leave, the bride shook the wonderful purse and sent a shower of gold pieces flying among the guests. So they all went home very well pleased.

The good ferryman and his marvellous wife lived most happily together. They never wanted for anything, and gave freely to all who came. He continued to ply his ferry-boat. But he now took all passengers over for nothing, and gave them each a piece of gold into the bargain.

Now there was a king over that country, who a year ago had just succeeded to his elder brother. He had heard of the ferryman, who was so marvellously rich, and wished to ascertain the truth of the story he had heard. He came on purpose to see for himself. But when he saw the ferry-man's beautiful young wife, he resolved to have her for himself, and determined to get rid of her husband somehow.

At that time there was an eclipse of the sun. The king sent for the ferryman, and told him he must find out the cause of this eclipse, or be put to death.

He came home in great distress to his wife, but she replied, 'Never mind, my dear. I will tell you what to do, and how to gratify the king's curiosity.'

So she gave him a wonderful ball of thread, which he was to throw before him, and follow the thread as it kept unwinding towards the East.

He went on a long way, over high mountains, deep rivers, and wide regions. At last he came to a ruined city, where a number of corpses were lying about unburied, tainting the air with pestilence.

The good man was sorry to see this, and took pains to summon men from the neighbouring cities, and get the bodies properly buried. He then resumed his journey.

He came at last to the ends of the earth. Here he found a magnificent golden palace, with an amber roof, and diamond doors and windows.

The ball of thread went straight into the palace, and the ferryman found himself in a vast apartment, where sat a very dignified old lady, spinning from a golden distaff.

'Wretched man! What are you here for?' she exclaimed, when she saw him. 'My son will come back presently and burn you up.'

He explained to her how he had been forced to come out of sheer necessity.

'Well, I must help you,' replied the old lady, who was the Mother of the Sun. 'Because you did good some days ago, in burying the inhabitants of that town when they were killed by a dragon. He journeys every day across the wide arch of heaven in a diamond car drawn by 12 grey horses with golden manes giving heat and light to the whole world. He will soon be back here, to rest for the night. . . . But . . . here he comes; hide yourself, and take care to observe what follows.'

Then, she changed her visitor into a ladybird and let him fly to the window.

Then the neighing of the wonderful horses and the rattling of chariot wheels were heard, and the bright Sun himself presently came in and stretching himself upon a coral bed remarked to his mother, 'I smell a human being here!'

'What nonsense you talk!' replied his mother. 'How could any human being come here? You know it is impossible.'

The Sun, as if he did not quite believe her, began to peer anxiously about the room.

'Don't be so restless,' said the old lady, 'but tell me why you suffered an eclipse a month or two ago.'

'How could I help it?' answered the Sun. 'When the dragon from the deep abyss attacked me, I had to fight him. Perhaps I would have been fighting with the monster now, if a wonderful mermaid had not come to help me. When she began to sing and looked at the dragon with her beautiful eyes, all his rage softened at once. He was absorbed in gazing upon her beauty. Meanwhile I burnt him to ashes, and threw them into the sea.'

The Sun then went to sleep, and his mother touched the ferryman again with her spindle. He then returned to his natural shape, and slipped out of the palace. Following the ball of thread, he reached home at last, and next day he went to the king and told him all.

But the king was so enchanted at the description of the beautiful sea-maiden that he ordered the ferryman to go and bring her to him, on pain of death.

He went home very sad to his wife, but she told him she would manage this also. So saying she gave him another ball of thread to show him which way to go, and she also gave him a carriage-load of costly ladies' apparel, jewels, and ornaments and told him what he was to do. They took leave of one another.

On the way, the ferryman met a youth riding on a fine grey horse, who asked, 'What have you got there, man?'

'A woman's wearing apparel, most costly and beautiful.' He had several dresses, not simply one.

'I say, give me some of those as a present for my intended, whom I am going to see. I can be of use to you, for I am the Storm-wind. I will come, whenever you call upon me thus, "Storm-wind! Storm-wind! Come with speed! Help me in my sudden need!"'

The ferryman gave him some of the most beautiful things he had, and the Storm-wind passed.

A little further on he met an old man, grey-haired but strong and vigorous-looking, who also said, 'What have you got there?'

'Women's garments costly and beautiful.'

'I am going to my daughter's wedding. She is to marry the Storm-wind. Give me something as a wedding present for her, and I will be of use to you. I am the Frost. If you need me call upon me thus, "Frost, I call thee. Come with speed. Help me in my sudden need!"'

The ferryman let him take all he wanted and went on. And now he came to the sea coast. Here the ball of thread stopped and would go no further.

The ferryman waded up to his waist into the sea and set up two high poles with cross-bars between them upon which he hung dresses of various colours, scarves, and ribbons, gold chains, diamond earrings and pins, shoes, and looking glasses, and then hid himself with his wonderful hook and line ready.

As soon as the morning rose from the sea, there appeared far away on the smooth waters, a silvery boat in which stood a beautiful maiden, with a golden oar in one hand, while with the other she gathered together her long golden hair. All the while singing so beautifully to the rising sun, that, if the ferryman had not quickly stopped his ears, he would have fallen into a delicious reverie and then asleep.

She sailed along a long time in her silver boat, and around her, golden fishes with rainbow wings and diamond eyes leaped and played. But all at once she perceived the rich clothes and ornaments hung up on the poles, and as she came nearer, the ferryman called out:

'Storm-wind! Storm-wind! Come with speed! Help me in my sudden need!'

'What do you want?' asked the Storm-wind.

The ferryman without answering him, called out, 'Frost, I call thee, come with speed. Help me in my sudden need!'

'What do you want?' asked the Frost.

'I want to capture the sea-maiden.'

Then the wind blew and blew so that the silver boat was capsized, and the frost breathed on the sea till it was frozen over.

Then the ferryman rushed up to the sea-maiden, entangling his hook in her golden hair, lifted her on his horse, and they rode off as swift as the wind after his wonderful ball of thread.

She kept weeping and lamenting all the way; but as soon as they reached the ferryman's home, and saw his wife, all her sorrow changed into joy. She laughed with delight, and threw herself into her arms.

It turned out that the two were sisters.

Next morning the ferryman went to court with both his wife and sister-in-law, and the king was so delighted with the beauty of the latter that he at once offered to marry her. But she could give him no answer until he had the Self-playing Guitar.

So the king ordered the ferryman to procure him this wonderful guitar, or he be put to death.

His wife told him what to do, and gave him a handkerchief of hers embroidered with gold, and she told him to use this in case of need.

Following the ball of thread, he came at last to a great lake, in the midst of which was a green island.

He began to wonder how he was to get there when he saw a boat approaching in which was an old man, with a long white beard, and he recognized him with delight as his former benefactor.

'How are you, ferryman?' he asked. 'Where are you going?'

'I am going wherever the ball of thread leads me, for I must fetch the Self-playing Guitar.'

'This guitar,' said the old man, 'belongs to Goldmore, the lord of that island. It is a difficult matter to have to deal with him; but perhaps you may succeed. You have often ferried me over the water. I will ferry you now.'

The old man pushed off, and they reached the island.

On arriving the ball of thread went straight into a palace where Goldmore came out to meet the traveller, and asked him where he was going and what he wanted.

He explained, 'I am come for the Self-playing Guitar.'

'I will only let you have it on condition that you do not go to sleep for three days and nights. And if you do, you will not only lose all chance of the Self-playing Guitar, but you must die.'

What could the poor man do, but agree to this?

So Goldmore conducted him to a great room and locked him in. The floor was strewn with sleepy-grass, so he fell asleep directly.

Next morning in came Goldmore, and on waking him up said, 'So you went to sleep! Very well, you shall die!'

And he touched a spring in the floor, and the unhappy ferryman fell down into an apartment beneath where the walls were of looking-glass, and there were great heaps of gold and precious stones lying about.

For three days and nights he lay there. He was fearfully hungry, and then it dawned upon him that he was to be starved to death!

He called out, and entreated in vain. Nobody answered, and though he had piles of gold and jewels about him, they could not purchase him a morsel of food.

He sought in vain for any means of exit. There was a window, of clearest crystal, but it was barred by a heavy iron grating. But the window looked into a garden where he could hear nightingales singing, doves cooing, and the murmur of a brook. But inside he saw only heaps of useless gold and jewels, and his own face, worn and haggard, reflected a thousand times.

He could now only pray for a speedy death, and took out a little iron cross which he had kept by him since his boyhood. But in doing so he also drew out the gold-embroidered handkerchief, given him by his wife and which he had quite forgotten till now.

Goldmore had been looking on, as he often did, from an opening in the ceiling to enjoy the sight of his prisoner's sufferings. All at once he recognized the handkerchief, as belonging to his own sister, the ferryman's wife.

He at once changed his treatment of his brother-in-law, as he had discovered him to be. He took him out of prison, led him to his own apartments, gave him food and drink, and the Self-playing Guitar into the bargain.

Coming home, the ferryman met his wife halfway.

'The ball of thread came home alone,' she explained, 'so I judged that some misfortune had befallen you, and I was coming to help you.'

He told her all his adventures, and they returned home together.

The king was eager to see and hear the Self-playing Guitar, so he ordered the ferryman, his wife, and her sister to come with it to the palace at once.

Now the property of this Self-playing Guitar was such that wherever its music was heard, the sick became well, those who were sad merry, ugly folks became handsome, sorceries were dissolved, and those who had been murdered rose from the dead and slew their murderers.

So when the king, having been told the charm to set the guitar playing, said the words, all the court began to be merry, and dance except the king himself! For all at once the door opened, the music ceased, and the figure of the late king stood up in his shroud, and said, 'I was the rightful possessor of the throne! And you, wicked brother, who caused me to be murdered, shall now reap your reward!'

So saying he breathed upon him, and the king fell dead on which the phantom vanished.

But as soon as they recovered from their fright, all the nobility who were present acclaimed the ferryman as their king.

The next day, after the burial of the late king, the beautiful sea-maiden, the beloved of the Sun, went back to the sea to float about in her silvery canoe in the company of the rainbow fishes and to rejoice in the sunbeams.

But the good ferryman and his wife lived happily ever after, as king and queen. And they gave a grand ball to the nobility and to the people. The Self-playing Guitar furnished the music, the wonderful purse scattered gold all the time, and the king entertained all the guests royally.

SIGNOR LATTANZIO

(ITALIAN)

They say there was a duke who wandered over the world seeking a beautiful maiden to make his wife.

After many years he came to an inn where was a lady, who asked him what he sought.

'I have journeyed half the earth over,' answered the duke, 'to find a wife to my fancy, and have not found one; and now I go back to my native city as I came.'

'How sad!' answered the lady. 'I have a daughter who is the most beautiful maiden that ever was made; but three fairies have taken possession of her, and locked her up in a casino in the Campagna, and no one can get to see her.'

'Only tell me where she is,' replied the duke, 'and I promise you I'll get to see her, in spite of all the fairies in the world.'

'It is useless!' replied the lady. 'So many have tried and failed. So will you.'

'Not I!' answered the duke. 'Tell me how they failed, and I will do otherwise.'

'I have told so many, and all say the same as you, and all go to seek her, but none ever come back.'

'Never mind! Tell it once again, and I promise you it shall be the last time, for I will surely come back.'

'If you are bent on sacrificing yourself uselessly,' proceeded the lady, 'this is the story. You must go to the mountain of Russia, and at the foot of it there will meet you three most beautiful maidens, who will come round you, and praise you, and flatter you, and pour out all manner of blandishments, and will ask you to go into their palace with them, and will entreat you so much that you will not be able to resist; then you will go into their palace with them, and they will turn you into a cat, for they are three fairies. But, on the other hand, if you can resist only for the space of one hour to all they will say to you, then you will have conquered, and they will be turned into cats, and you will have free access to my daughter to release her.'

'I will go,' said the duke firmly; and he rose up and went his way to the mountain of Russia.

'Now, if all these other men have failed in this same attempt,' he mused within himself as he went along, 'it behoves me to be prudent. I know what I will do; I will put a bandage over my eyes, and then I shan't see the fairies, and their blandishments will have no power over me.' And so he did.

Then the fairies came out to him and said, 'Signor Lattanzio! welcome, welcome! how fair you are; do take the bandage off and let us see you; how noble you look. Do let us see your face? We are dying to have you with us!'

But the duke remained firm, and seemed to take no heed, though their voices were so soft and persuasive that he longed to look at them, or even to lift up one corner of the bandage and take a peep. But he remained firm.

'Signor Lattanzio! Signor Lattanzio! Don't be so ungallant,' pursued the fairies. 'Here are we at your feet, as it were, begging you to give us your company, and you will not so much as speak to us, or even look at us!'

But the duke remained firm, and seemed to take no heed, though his head was turned by their accents, and he felt that if he could only go with them as they wished he should want no more. But he remained firm.

'Signor Lattanzio! Signor Lattanzio! Signor Lattanzio!' cried the three fairies disdainfully, for now they began to suspect in right good earnest that at least one had come who was too strong for them. 'The fact is you are afraid of us. If you are a man, show you have no fear, and come and talk with us.'

But the duke remained firm, though a vanity, which had nearly lost him, whispered that it would be a grander triumph to look them in the face and yet resist them, than to conquer without having ventured to look at them, yet prudence prevailed, and he remained firm.

So they went on, and the duke felt that the hour was drawing to a close. He took out his repeater and struck it, and the hour of trial was over.

'Traitor!' cried the three fairies, and in the same instant they were turned into cats. Then the duke went into their palace, and took their wand, and with it he could open the gates of the casino where the lady's daughter was imprisoned.

When he saw her, he found her indeed fairer than the fairest; fairer even than his conception.

When, therefore, with the wand he had restored all the cats that were upon the mountain to their natural shapes as those that had failed in their enterprise, he took her home with him to be his wife.

THE THREE ORANGES

(ITALIAN)

There was once, I don't know where, a king, who had three sons. They had reached a marriageable age, but could not find anyone who suited them, or someone who pleased their father. 'Go, my sons, and look around in the world,' said the king, 'and try to find wives somewhere else.' The three sons went away, and at bedtime they came to a small cottage, in which a very, very old woman lived. She asked them about the object of their journey, which the princes readily communicated to her. The old woman provided them with the necessaries for the journey as well as she could. Before taking leave of her guests, she gave them an orange each, with instructions to cut them open only in the neighbourhood of water, or else they would suffer great, very great damage. The three princes started on their way again, and the eldest was not able to restrain his curiosity as to what sort of fruit it could be, or to conceive what harm could possibly happen if he cut it open in a place where there was no water near. He cut into the orange, and lo!, a beautiful girl, such as he had never seen before, came out of it. She exclaimed, 'Water! Let me have some water, or I shall die on the spot.' The prince ran in every direction to get water, but could not find any, and the beautiful girl died in a short time as the old woman had said. The princes went on, and now the younger one began to be inquisitive as to what could be in his orange.

They had just sat down to luncheon on a plain, under a tall, leafy tree, when it appeared to them that they could see a lake not very far off. 'Supposing there is a girl in the fruit, I can fulfil her wish,' he thought to himself. Not being able to restrain his curiosity any longer as to what sort of girl there could be inside, he cut his orange, and lo! a girl, very much more beautiful than the first, stepped out of it and called out for water in order to save her life. He had previously sent his brother to what he thought was a lake. As he could not wait for his return with the water, he ran off himself, quite out of breath, but the further he ran, the further the lake appeared to be off because it was only a mirage. He rushed back to the tree nearly beside himself in order to see whether the girl was yet alive, but he only found her body lifeless, and quite cold.

The two elder brothers, seeing that they had lost what they had been searching for and had given up all hope of finding a prettier one, returned in great sorrow to their father's house, and the youngest continued his journey alone. He wandered about until, after much fatigue, he came to the neighbourhood of some town, where he found a well. He had no doubt that there was a girl in his orange also, so he took courage and cut it. Indeed, a girl, who was a hundred times prettier than the first two, came out of it. She called out for water, and the prince gave her some at once. Death had no power over her. The prince now hurried into the town to purchase rich dresses for his love. So that no harm might happen to her during his absence, he made her sit up in a tree with dense foliage, the boughs of which overhung the well.

As soon as the prince left, a gipsy woman came to the well for water. She looked into the well and saw in the water the beautiful face of the girl in the tree. At first she fancied that she saw the image of her own face and felt very much flattered. But she soon found out her mistake, and looking about discovered the pretty girl in the tree. 'What are you waiting for, my pretty maid?' inquired the gipsy woman with a cunning face. The girl told her story, whereupon the gipsy woman, shamming kindness, climbed up the tree, pushed the pretty girl into the well, and took her place in the tree when the pretty girl sank. The next moment a beautiful little gold fish appeared swimming in the water. The gipsy woman recognized it as the girl, and, being afraid that it might be dangerous to her, tried to catch it when suddenly the prince appeared with the costly dresses. So at once she laid her plans to deceive him. The prince immediately noticed the difference between her and the girl he had left. But she succeeded in making him believe that for a time after having left the fairy world, she had to lose her beauty, but that the more he loved her, the sooner she would recover it. So the prince was satisfied, and he went home to his father's house with the woman he found and loved her in hopes of her regaining her former beauty. The good food and happy life, and also the pretty dresses, improved the sunburnt woman's looks a little. The prince, imagining that his wife's prediction was going to be fulfilled, felt more attached to her, and was anxious to carry out all her wishes.

The woman, however, could not forget the little gold fish, and therefore feigned illness, saying that she would not get better till she had eaten of the liver of a gold fish, which was to be found in a well. The prince had the fish caught at once, and the princess, having partaken of the liver, got better, and felt more cheerful than before. It happened, however, that one scale of the fish had been cast out in the courtyard with the water, and from it, a beautiful tree began to grow. The princess noticed it and found how the tree got there and again fell ill, and she said that she could not get better until they burnt the tree and cooked her something by the flames. This wish also was fulfilled, and she got better. It happened, however, that one of the woodcutters took a square piece of the timber home to his wife, who used it as a lid for a milk jug. These people lived not very far from the royal palace, and were poor. The woman herself kept the house, and did all the servants' work.

One day she left her house very early without having put anything in order and without having done her usual household work. When she came home in the evening, she found all that her house was clean and in the best order. She was very much astonished and could not imagine how it came to pass. It happened thus on several days whenever she had not put her house in order before going out. In order to find out how these things were accomplished, one day she purposely left her home in disorder. She did not go far but remained outside peeping through the keyhole to see what would happen. As soon as everything became quiet in the house, the woman saw that the lid of the milk jug, which was standing in the window, began to move with gentle noise. In a few moments a beautiful fairy stepped out of it, who first combed her golden tresses, and performed her toilet and afterwards put the whole house in order. The woman, in order to trap the fairy before she had time to retransform herself, opened the door abruptly. They both seemed astonished, but the kind and encouraging words of the woman soon dispelled the girl's fear. Now she related her whole story, how she came into the world, how she became a gold fish, and then a tree, and how she used to walk out of the wooden lid of the milk jug to tidy the house. She also enlightened the woman as to who the present Princess was. The woman listened to all in great astonishment. In order to prevent the girl from slipping back into the lid, she threw the wooden jug into the fire. She went to the prince at once, and told him the whole story.

The prince had already grown suspicious about his wife's beauty, which had been very long in returning, and now he was quite sure that she was a cheat. He sent for the girl and recognized her at once as the pretty fairy whom he had left in the tree. The gipsy woman was put into the pillory, and the prince married the pretty girl. They lived ever after in happiness.

FELICIA AND THE POT OF PINKS

(FRENCH)

Once upon a time there was a poor labourer who, feeling that he had not much longer to live, wished to divide his possessions between his son and daughter, whom he loved dearly.

So he called them to him, and said: 'As her dowry your mother brought me two stools and a straw bed; I have, besides, a hen, a pot of pinks, and a silver ring, which were given me by a noble lady who once lodged in my poor cottage. When she went away she said to me:

'Be careful of my gifts, good man; see that you do not lose the ring or forget to water the pinks. As for your daughter, I promise you that she shall be more beautiful than anyone you ever saw in your life; call her Felicia, and when she grows up give her the ring and the pot of pinks to console her for her poverty. Take them both, then, my dear child,' he added, 'and your brother shall have everything else.'

The two children seemed quite contented, and when their father died they wept for him, and divided his possessions as he had told them. Felicia believed that her brother loved her, but when she sat down upon one of the stools he said angrily:

'Keep your pot of pinks and your ring, but let my things alone. I like order in my house.'

Felicia, who was very gentle, said nothing, but stood up crying quietly while Bruno, for that was her brother's name, sat comfortably by the fire. Presently, when supper time came, Bruno had a delicious egg, and he threw the shell to Felicia, saying:

'There, that is all I can give you. If you don't like it, go out and catch frogs; there are plenty of them in the marsh close by.' Felicia did not answer, but she cried more bitterly than ever, and went away to her own little room. She found it filled with the sweet scent of the pinks, and, going up to them, she said sadly:

'Beautiful pinks, you are so sweet and so pretty. You are the only comfort I have left. Be very sure that I will take care of you, and water you well, and never allow any cruel hand to tear you from your stems.'

As she leaned over them she noticed that they were very dry. So taking her pitcher, she ran off in the clear moonlight to the fountain, which was at some distance. When she reached it she sat down upon the brink to rest, but she had hardly done so when she saw a stately lady coming toward her, surrounded by numbers of attendants. Six maids of honour carried her train, and she leaned upon the arm of another.

When they came near the fountain a canopy was spread for her, under which was placed a sofa of cloth-of-gold, and presently a dainty supper was served, upon a table covered with dishes of gold and crystal, while the wind in the trees and the falling water of the fountain murmured the softest music.

Felicia was hidden in the shade, too much astonished by all she saw to venture to move; but in a few moments the Queen said, 'I fancy I see a shepherdess near that tree; bid her come hither.'

So Felicia came forward and saluted the Queen timidly, but with so much grace that all were surprised.

'What are you doing here, my pretty child?' asked the Queen. 'Are you not afraid of robbers?'

'Ah! madam,' said Felicia, 'a poor shepherdess who has nothing to lose does not fear robbers.'

'You are not very rich, then?' said the Queen, smiling.

'I am so poor,' answered Felicia, 'that a pot of pinks and a silver ring are my only possessions in the world.'

'But you have a heart,' said the Queen. 'What should you say if anybody wanted to steal that?'

'I do not know what it is like to lose one's heart, madam,' she replied, 'but I have always heard that without a heart one cannot live, and if it is broken one must die; and in spite of my poverty I should be sorry not to live.'

'You are quite right to take care of your heart, pretty one,' said the Queen. 'But tell me, have you had supper?'

'No, madam,' answered Felicia, 'my brother ate all the supper there was.'

Then the Queen ordered that a place should be made for her at the table, and herself loaded Felicia's plate with good things; but she was too much astonished to be hungry.

'I want to know what you were doing at the fountain so late?' said the Queen presently.

'I came to fetch a pitcher of water for my pinks, madam,' she answered, stooping to pick up the pitcher which stood beside her; but when she showed it to the Queen she was amazed to see that it had turned to gold, all sparkling with great diamonds, and the water, of which it was full, was more fragrant than the sweetest roses. She was afraid to take it until the Queen said, 'It is yours, Felicia. Go and water your pinks with it, and let it remind you that the Queen of the Woods is your friend.'

The shepherdess threw herself at the Queen's feet, and thanked her humbly for her gracious words.

'Ah! madam,' she cried. 'If I might beg you to stay here a moment I would run and fetch my pot of pinks for you – they could not fall into better hands.'

'Go, Felicia,' said the Queen, stroking her cheek softly, 'I will wait here until you come back.'

So Felicia took up her pitcher and ran to her little room, but while she had been away Bruno had gone in and taken the pot of pinks, leaving a great cabbage in its place. When she saw the unlucky cabbage Felicia was much distressed, and did not know what to do, but at last she ran back to the fountain, and, kneeling before the Queen, said, 'Madam, Bruno has stolen my pot of pinks, so I have nothing but my silver ring; but I beg you to accept it as a proof of my gratitude.'

'But if I take your ring, my pretty shepherdess,' said the Queen, 'you will have nothing left; and what will you do then?'

'Ah! madam,' she answered simply, 'if I have your friendship I shall do very well.'

So the Queen took the ring and put it on her finger, and mounted her chariot, which was made of coral studded with emeralds, and drawn by six milk-white horses. Felicia looked after her until the winding of the forest path hid her from her sight, and then she went back to the cottage thinking over all the wonderful things that had happened.

The first thing she did when she reached her room was to throw the cabbage out of the window. But she was very much surprised to hear an odd little voice cry out 'Oh! I am half killed!' and could not tell where it came from, because cabbages do not generally speak.

As soon as it was light, Felicia, who was very unhappy about her pot of pinks, went out to look for it, and the first thing she found was the unfortunate cabbage. She gave it a push with her foot, saying: 'What are you doing here, and how dared you put yourself in the place of my pot of pinks?'

'If I hadn't been carried,' replied the cabbage, 'you may be very sure that I shouldn't have thought of going there.'

It made her shiver with fright to hear the cabbage talk, but he went on, 'If you will be good enough to plant me by my comrades again, I can tell you where your pinks are at this moment – hidden in Bruno's bed!'

Felicia was in despair when she heard this, not knowing how she was to get them back. But she replanted the cabbage very kindly in his old place, and, as she finished doing it, she saw Bruno's hen, and said, catching hold of it:

'Come here, horrid little creature! You shall suffer for all the unkind things my brother has done to me.'

'Ah! shepherdess,' said the hen, 'don't kill me; I am rather a gossip, and I can tell you some surprising things that you will like to hear. Don't imagine that you are the daughter of the poor labourer who brought you up. Your mother was a queen who had six girls already, and the King threatened that unless she had a son who could inherit his kingdom she should have her head cut off.

'So when the Queen had another little daughter she was quite frightened, and agreed with her sister (who was a fairy) to exchange her for the fairy's little son. Now the Queen had been shut up in a great tower by the King's orders, and when a great many days went by and still she heard nothing from the Fairy she made her escape from the window by means of a rope ladder, taking her little baby with her. After wandering about until she was half dead with cold and fatigue she reached this cottage. I was the labourer's wife, and was a good nurse, and the Queen gave you into my charge, and told me all her misfortunes, and then died before she had time to say what was to become of you.

'As I never in all my life could keep a secret, I could not help telling this strange tale to my neighbours, and one day when a beautiful lady came here, I told it to her also. When I had finished she touched me with a wand she held in her hand, and instantly I became a hen, and there was an end of my talking! I was very sad, and my husband, who was out when it happened, never knew what had become of me. After seeking me everywhere he believed that I must have been drowned, or eaten up by wild beasts in the forest. That same lady came here once more, and commanded that you should be called Felicia, and left the ring and the pot of pinks to be given to you. While she was in the house 25 of the King's guards came to search for you, doubtless meaning to kill you. But she muttered a few words, and immediately they all turned into cabbages. It was one of them whom you threw out of your window yesterday.

'I don't know how it was that he could speak – I have never heard either of them say a word before, nor have I been able to do it myself until now.'

The Princess was greatly astonished at the hen's story, and said kindly: 'I am truly sorry for you, my poor nurse, and wish it was in my power to restore you to your real form. But we must not despair; it seems to me, after what you have told me, that something must be going to happen soon. Just now, however, I must go and look for my pinks, which I love better than anything in the world.'

Bruno had gone out into the forest, never thinking that Felicia would search in his room for the pinks, and she was delighted by his unexpected absence, and thought to get them back without further trouble. But as soon as she entered the room she saw a terrible army of rats who were guarding the straw bed. When she attempted to approach it they sprang at her, biting and scratching furiously. Quite terrified, she drew back, crying out, 'Oh! My dear pinks, how can you stay here in such bad company?'

Then she suddenly thought of the pitcher of water, and, hoping that it might have some magic power, she ran to fetch it, and sprinkled a few drops over the fierce-looking swarm of rats. In a moment not a tail or a whisker was to be seen. Each one had made for his hole as fast as his legs could carry him, so that the Princess could safely take her pot of pinks. She found them nearly dying for want of water, and hastily poured all that was left in the pitcher upon them. As she bent over them, enjoying their delicious scent, a soft voice, that seemed to rustle among the leaves, said:

'Lovely Felicia, the day has come at last when I may have the happiness of telling you how even the flowers love you and rejoice in your beauty.'

The Princess, quite overcome by the strangeness of hearing a cabbage, a hen, and a pink speak, and by the terrible sight of an army of rats, suddenly became very pale, and fainted away.

At this moment in came Bruno. Working hard in the heat had not improved his temper, and when he saw that Felicia had succeeded in finding her pinks he was so angry that he dragged her out into the garden and shut the door upon her. The fresh air soon made her open her pretty eyes, and there before her stood the Queen of the Woods, looking as charming as ever.

'You have a bad brother,' she said 'I saw he turned you out. Shall I punish him for it?'

'Ah! no, madam,' she said, 'I am not angry with him.'

'But supposing he was not your brother, after all, what would you say then?' asked the Queen.

'Oh! but I think he must be,' said Felicia.

'What!' said the Queen, 'have you not heard that you are a Princess?'

'I was told so a little while ago, madam, but how could I believe it without a single proof?'

'Ah! dear child,' said the Queen, 'the way you speak assures me that, in spite of your humble upbringing, you are indeed a real princess. I can save you from being treated in such a way again.'

She was interrupted at this moment by the arrival of a very handsome young man. He wore a coat of green velvet fastened with emerald clasps, and had a crown of pinks on his head. He knelt upon one knee and kissed the Queen's hand.

'Ah!' she cried, 'my pink, my dear son, what a happiness to see you restored to your natural shape by Felicia's aid!' and she embraced him joyfully. Then, turning to Felicia, she said:

'Charming Princess, I know all the hen told you, but you cannot have heard that the zephyrs, to whom was entrusted the task of carrying my son to the tower where the Queen, your mother, so anxiously waited for him, left him instead in a garden of flowers, while they flew off to tell your mother. Whereupon a fairy with whom I had quarrelled changed him into a pink, and I could do nothing to prevent it.

'You can imagine how angry I was, and how I tried to find some means of undoing the mischief she had done. But there was no help for it. I could only bring Prince Pink to the place where you were being brought up, hoping that when you grew up he might love you, and by your care be restored to his natural form. And you see everything has come right, as I hoped it would. Your giving me the silver ring was the sign that the power of the charm was nearly over, and my enemy's last chance was to frighten you with her army of rats. That she did not succeed in doing; so now, my dear Felicia, if you will be married to my son with this silver ring your future happiness is certain. Do you think him handsome and amiable enough to be willing to marry him?'

'Madam,' replied Felicia, blushing, 'you overwhelm me with your kindness. I know that you are my mother's sister, and that by your art you turned the soldiers who were sent to kill me into cabbages, and my nurse into a hen, and that you do me only too much honour in proposing that I shall marry your son. How can I explain to you the cause of my hesitation? I feel, for the first time in my life, how happy it would make me to be beloved. Can you indeed give me the Prince's heart?'

'It is yours already, lovely Princess!' he cried, taking her hand in his. 'But for the horrible enchantment which kept me silent I should have told you long ago how dearly I love you.'

This made the Princess very happy, and the Queen, who could not bear to see her dressed like a poor shepherdess, touched her with her wand, saying, 'I wish you to be attired as befits your rank and beauty.' Immediately the Princess's cotton dress became a magnificent robe of silver brocade embroidered with carbuncles, and her soft dark hair was encircled by a crown of diamonds, from which floated a clear white veil. With her bright eyes, and the charming colour in her cheeks, she was altogether such a dazzling sight that the Prince could hardly bear it.

'How pretty you are, Felicia!' he cried. 'Don't keep me in suspense. I entreat you, say that you will marry me.'

'Ah!' said the Queen, smiling, 'I think she will not refuse now.'

Just then Bruno, who was going back to his work, came out of the cottage, and thought he must be dreaming when he saw Felicia. But she called him very kindly, and begged the Queen to take pity on him.

'What!' she said. 'When he was so unkind to you?'

'Ah! madam,' said the Princess, 'I am so happy that I should like everybody else to be happy too.'

The Queen kissed her, and said, 'Well, to please you, let me see what I can do for this cross Bruno.' With a wave of her wand she turned the poor little cottage into a splendid palace, full of treasures; only the two stools and the straw bed remained just as they were, to remind him of his former poverty. Then the Queen touched Bruno himself, and made him gentle and polite and grateful, and he thanked her and the Princess a thousand times. Lastly, the Queen restored the hen and the cabbages to their natural forms, and left them all very contented. The Prince and Princess were married as soon as possible with great splendour, and lived happily ever after.

THE DWARFIE STONE

(SCOTTISH)

Far up in a green valley in the Island of Hoy stands an immense boulder. It is hollow inside, and the natives of these northern islands call it the Dwarfie Stone, because long centuries ago, so the legend has it, Snorro the Dwarf lived there.

Nobody knew where Snorro came from, or how long he had dwelt in the dark chamber inside the Dwarfie Stone. All that they knew about him was that he was a little man, with a queer, twisted, deformed body and a face of marvellous beauty, which never seemed to look any older, but was always smiling and young.

Men said that this was because Snorro's father had been a Fairy, and not a denizen of earth, who had bequeathed to his son the gift of perpetual youth, but nobody knew whether this were true or not, for the Dwarf had inhabited the Dwarfie Stone long before the oldest man or woman in Hoy had been born.

One thing was certain, however: he had inherited from his mother, whom all men agreed had been mortal, the dangerous qualities of vanity and ambition. And the longer he lived the more vain and ambitious did he become, until at last he always carried a mirror of polished steel round his neck, into which he constantly looked in order to see the reflection of his handsome face.

And he would not attend to the country people who came to seek his help, unless they bowed themselves humbly before him and spoke to him as if he were a King.

I say that the country people sought his help, for he spent his time, or appeared to spend it, in collecting herbs and simples on the hillsides, which he carried home with him to his dark abode, and distilled medicines and potions from them, which he sold to his neighbours at wondrous high prices.

He was also the possessor of a wonderful leathern-covered book, clasped with clasps of brass, over which he would pore for hours together, and out of which he would tell the simple Islanders their fortunes, if they would.

For they feared the book almost as much as they feared Snorro himself, for it was whispered that it had once belonged to Odin, and they crossed themselves for protection as they named the mighty Enchanter.

But all the time they never guessed the real reason why Snorro chose to live in the Dwarfie Stone.

I will tell you why he did so. Not very far from the Stone there was a curious hill, shaped exactly like a wart. It was known as the Wart Hill of Hoy, and men said that somewhere in the side of it was hidden a wonderful carbuncle, which, when it was found, would bestow on its finder marvellous magic gifts – Health, Wealth, and Happiness. Everything, in fact, that a human being could desire.

And the curious thing about this carbuncle was, that it was said that it could be seen at certain times, if only the people who were looking for it were at the right spot at the right moment.

Now Snorro had made up his mind that he would find this wonderful stone, so, while he pretended to spend all his time in reading his great book or distilling medicines from his herbs, he was really keeping a keen look-out during his wanderings, noting every tuft of grass or piece of rock under which it might be hidden.

And at night, when everyone else was asleep, he would creep out, with pickaxe and spade, to turn over the rocks or dig over the turf, in the hope of finding the long-sought-for treasure underneath them.

He was always accompanied on these occasions by an enormous grey-headed Raven, who lived in the cave along with him, and who was his bosom friend and companion. The Islanders feared this bird of ill omen as much, perhaps, as they feared its Master; for, although they went to consult Snorro in all their difficulties and perplexities, and bought medicines and love-potions from him, they always looked upon him with a certain dread, feeling that there was something weird and uncanny about him.

Now, at the time we are speaking of, Orkney was governed by two Earls, who were half-brothers. Paul, the elder, was a tall, handsome man, with dark hair, and eyes like sloes. All the country people loved him, for he was so skilled in knightly exercises, and had such a sweet and loving nature, that no one could help being fond of him. Old people's eyes would brighten at the sight of him, and the little children would run out to greet him as he rode by their mothers' doors.

And this was the more remarkable because, with all his winning manner, he had such a lack of conversation that men called him Paul the Silent, or Paul the Taciturn.

Harold, on the other hand, was as different from his brother as night is from day. He was fair-haired and blue-eyed, and he had gained for himself the name of Harold the Orator, because he was always free of speech and ready with his tongue.

But for all this he was not a favourite. For he was haughty, and jealous, and quick-tempered, and the old folks' eyes did not brighten at the sight of him, and the babes, instead of toddling out to greet him, hid their faces in their mothers' skirts when they saw him coming.

Harold could not help knowing that the people liked his silent brother best, and the knowledge made him jealous of him, so a coldness sprang up between them.

Now it chanced, one summer, that Earl Harold went on a visit to the King of Scotland, accompanied by his mother, the Countess Helga, and her sister, the Countess Fraukirk.

And while he was at Court he met a charming young Irish lady, the Lady Morna, who had come from Ireland to Scotland to attend upon the Scottish Queen. She was so sweet, and good, and gentle that Earl Harold's heart was won, and he made up his mind that she, and only she, should be his bride.

But although he had paid her much attention, Lady Morna had sometimes caught glimpses of his jealous temper; she had seen an evil expression in his eyes, and had heard him speak sharply to his servants, and she had no wish to marry him. So, to his great amazement, she refused the honour which he offered her, and told him that she would prefer to remain as she was.

Earl Harold ground his teeth in silent rage, but he saw that it was no use pressing his suit at that moment. So what he could not obtain by his own merits he determined to obtain by guile.

Accordingly he begged his mother to persuade the Lady Morna to go back with them on a visit, hoping that when she was alone with him in Orkney, he would be able to overcome her prejudice against him, and induce her to become his wife. And all the while he never remembered his brother Paul; or, if he did, he never thought it possible that he could be his rival.

But that was just the very thing that happened. The Lady Morna, thinking no evil, accepted the Countess Helga's invitation, and no sooner had the party arrived back in Orkney than Paul, charmed with the grace and beauty of the fair Irish Maiden, fell head over ears in love with her. And the Lady Morna, from the very first hour that she saw him, returned his love.

Of course this state of things could not long go on hidden, and when Harold realized what had happened his anger and jealousy knew no bounds. Seizing a dagger, he rushed up to the turret where his brother was sitting in his private apartments, and threatened to stab him to the heart if he did not promise to give up all thoughts of winning the lovely stranger.

But Paul met him with pleasant words.

'Calm thyself, Brother,' he said. 'It is true that I love the lady, but that is no proof that I shall win her. Is it likely that she will choose me, whom all men name Paul the Silent, when she hath the chance of marrying you, whose tongue moves so swiftly that to you is given the proud title of Harold the Orator?'

At these words Harold's vanity was flattered, and he thought that, after all, his step-brother was right, and that he had a very small chance, with his meagre gift of speech, of being successful in his suit. So he threw down his dagger, and, shaking hands with him, begged him to pardon his unkind thoughts, and went down the winding stair again in high good-humour with himself and all the world.

By this time it was coming near to the Feast of Yule, and at that Festival it was the custom for the Earl and his Court to leave Kirkwall for some weeks, and go to the great Palace of Orphir, nine miles distant. And in order to see that everything was ready, Earl Paul took his departure some days before the others.

The evening before he left he chanced to find the Lady Morna sitting alone in one of the deep windows of the great hall. She had been weeping, for she was full of sadness at the thought of his departure; and at the sight of her distress the kind-hearted young Earl could no longer contain himself, but, folding her in his arms, he whispered to her how much he loved her, and begged her to promise to be his wife.

She agreed willingly. Hiding her rosy face on his shoulder, she confessed that she had loved him from the very first day that she had seen him; and ever since that moment she had determined that, if she could not wed him, she would wed no other man.

For a little time they sat together, rejoicing in their new-found happiness. Then Earl Paul sprang to his feet.

'Let us go and tell the good news to my mother and my brother,' he said. 'Harold may be disappointed at first, for I know, Sweetheart, he would fain have had thee for his own. But his good heart will soon overcome all that, and he will rejoice with us also.'

But the Lady Morna shook her head. She knew, better than her lover, what Earl Harold's feeling would be; and she would fain put off the evil hour.

'Let us hold our peace till after Yule,' she pleaded. 'It will be a joy to keep our secret to ourselves for a little space; there will be time enough then to let all the world know.'

Rather reluctantly, Earl Paul agreed; and next day he set off for the Palace at Orphir, leaving his lady-love behind him.

Little he guessed the danger he was in! For, all unknown to him, his step-aunt, Countess Fraukirk, had chanced to be in the hall, the evening before, hidden behind a curtain, and she had overheard every word that Morna and he had spoken, and her heart was filled with black rage.

For she was a hard, ambitious woman, and she had always hated the young Earl, who was no blood-relation to her, and who stood in the way of his brother, her own nephew; for, if Paul were only dead, Harold would be the sole Earl of Orkney.

And now that he had stolen the heart of the Lady Morna, whom her own nephew loved, her hate and anger knew no bounds. She had hastened off to her sister's chamber as soon as the lovers had parted; and there the two women had remained talking together till the chilly dawn broke in the sky.

Next day a boat went speeding over the narrow channel of water that separates Pomona (on the mainland) from Hoy. In it sat a woman, but who she was, or what she was like, no one could say, for she was covered from head to foot with a black cloak, and her face was hidden behind a thick, dark veil.

Snorro the Dwarf knew her, even before she laid aside her trappings, for Countess Fraukirk was no stranger to him. In the course of her long life she had often had occasion to seek his aid to help her in her evil deeds, and she had always paid him well for his services in yellow gold. He therefore welcomed her gladly; but when he had heard the nature of her errand his smiling face grew grave again, and he shook his head.

'I have served thee well, Lady, in the past,' he said, 'but methinks that this thing goeth beyond my courage. For to compass an Earl's death is a weighty matter, especially when he is so well beloved as is the Earl Paul.

'Thou knowest why I have taken up my abode in this lonely spot – how I hope some day to light upon the magic carbuncle. Thou knowest also how the people fear me, and hate me too, forsooth. And if the young Earl died, and suspicion fell on me, I must needs fly the Island, for my life would not be worth a grain of sand. Then my chance of success would be gone. Nay! I cannot do it, Lady; I cannot do it.'

But the wily Countess offered him much gold, and bribed him higher and higher, first with wealth, then with success, and lastly she promised to obtain for him a high post at the Court of the King of Scotland; and at that his ambition stirred within him, his determination gave way, and he consented to do what she asked.

'I will summon my magic loom,' he said, 'and weave a piece of cloth of finest texture and of marvellous beauty; and before I weave it I will so poison the thread with a magic potion that, when it is fashioned into a garment, whoever puts it on will die ere he hath worn it many minutes.'

'Thou art a clever knave,' answered the Countess, a cruel smile lighting up her evil face, 'and thou shalt be rewarded. Let me have a couple of yards of this wonderful web, and I will make a bonnie waistcoat for my fine young Earl and give it to him as a Yuletide gift. Then I reckon that he will not see the year out.'

'That will he not,' said Dwarf Snorro, with a malicious grin; and the two parted, after arranging that the piece of cloth should be delivered at the Palace of Orphir on the day before Christmas Eve.

Now, when the Countess Fraukirk had been away upon her wicked errand, strange things were happening at the Castle at Kirkwall. For Harold, encouraged by his brother's absence, offered his heart and hand once more to the Lady Morna. Once more she refused him, and in order to make sure that the scene should not be repeated, she told him that she had plighted her troth to his brother. When he heard that this was so, rage and fury were like to devour him. Mad with anger, he rushed from her presence, flung himself upon his horse, and rode away in the direction of the sea shore.

While he was galloping wildly along, his eyes fell on the snow-clad hills of Hoy rising up across the strip of sea that divided the one island from the other. And his thoughts flew at once to Snorro the Dwarf, who he had had occasion, as well as his step-aunt, to visit in bygone days.

'I have it,' he cried. 'Stupid fool that I was not to think of it at once. I will go to Snorro, and buy from him a love-potion, which will make my Lady Morna hate my precious brother and turn her thoughts kindly towards me.'

So he made haste to hire a boat, and soon he was speeding over the tossing waters on his way to the Island of Hoy. When he arrived there he hurried up the lonely valley to where the Dwarfie Stone stood, and he had no difficulty in finding its uncanny occupant, for Snorro was standing at the hole that served as a door, his raven on his shoulder, gazing placidly at the setting sun.

A curious smile crossed his face when, hearing the sound of approaching footsteps, he turned round and his eyes fell on the young noble.

'What bringeth thee here, Sir Earl?' he asked gaily, for he scented more gold.

'I come for a love-potion,' said Harold; and without more ado he told the whole story to the Wizard. 'I will pay thee for it,' he added, 'if thou wilt give it to me quickly.'

Snorro looked at him from head to foot. 'Blind must the maiden be, Sir Orator,' he said, 'who needeth a love-potion to make her fancy so gallant a Knight.'

Earl Harold laughed angrily. 'It is easier to catch a sunbeam than a woman's roving fancy,' he replied. 'I have no time for jesting. For, hearken, old man, there is a proverb that saith, "Time and tide wait for no man," so I need not expect the tide to wait for me. The potion I must have, and that instantly.'

Snorro saw that he was in earnest, so without a word he entered his dwelling, and in a few minutes returned with a small phial in his hand, which was full of a rosy liquid.

'Pour the contents of this into the Lady Morna's wine-cup,' he said, 'and I warrant thee that before four-and-twenty hours have passed she will love thee better than thou lovest her now.'

Then he waved his hand, as if to dismiss his visitor, and disappeared into his dwelling-place.

Earl Harold made all speed back to the Castle; but it was not until one or two days had elapsed that he found a chance to pour the love-potion into the Lady Morna's wine-cup. But at last, one night at supper, he found an opportunity of doing so, and, waving away the little page-boy, he handed it to her himself.

She raised it to her lips, but she only made a pretence at drinking, for she had seen the hated Earl fingering the cup, and she feared some deed of treachery. When he had gone back to his seat she managed to pour the whole of the wine on the floor, and smiled to herself at the look of satisfaction that came over Harold's face as she put down the empty cup.

His satisfaction increased, for from that moment she felt so afraid of him that she treated him with great kindness, hoping that by doing so she would keep in his good graces until the Court moved to Orphir, and her own true love could protect her.

Harold, on his side, was delighted with her graciousness, for he felt certain that the charm was beginning to work, and that his hopes would soon be fulfilled.

A week later the Court removed to the Royal Palace at Orphir, where Earl Paul had everything in readiness for the reception of his guests.

Of course he was overjoyed to meet Lady Morna again, and she was overjoyed to meet him, for she felt that she was now safe from the unwelcome attentions of Earl Harold.

But to Earl Harold the sight of their joy was as gall and bitterness, and he could scarcely contain himself, although he still trusted in the efficacy of Snorro the Dwarf's love-potion.

As for Countess Fraukirk and Countess Helga, they looked forward eagerly to the time when the magic web would arrive, out of which they hoped to fashion a fatal gift for Earl Paul.

At last, the day before Christmas Eve, the two wicked women were sitting in the Countess Helga's chamber talking of the time when Earl Harold would rule alone in Orkney, when a tap came to the window, and on looking round they saw Dwarf Snorro's grey-headed Raven perched on the sill, a sealed packet in its beak.

They opened the casement, and with a hoarse croak the creature let the packet drop on to the floor; then it flapped its great wings and rose slowly into the air again, its head turned in the direction of Hoy.

With fingers that trembled with excitement they broke the seals and undid the packet. It contained a piece of the most beautiful material that anyone could possibly imagine, woven in all the colours of the rainbow, and sparkling with gold and jewels.

''Twill make a bonnie waistcoat,' exclaimed Countess Fraukirk, with an unholy laugh. 'The Silent Earl will be a braw man when he gets it on.'

Then, without more ado, they set to work to cut out and sew the garment. All that night they worked, and all next day, till late in the afternoon, when they were putting in the last stitches, hurried footsteps were heard ascending the winding staircase, and Earl Harold burst open the door.

His cheeks were red with passion, and his eyes were bright, for he could not but notice that, now that she was safe at Orphir under her true love's protection, the Lady Morna's manner had grown cold and distant again, and he was beginning to lose faith in Snorro's charm.

Angry and disappointed, he had sought his mother's room to pour out his story of vexation to her.

He stopped short, however, when he saw the wonderful waistcoat lying on the table, all gold and silver and shining colours. It was like a fairy garment, and its beauty took his breath away.

'For whom hast thou purchased that?' he asked, hoping to hear that it was intended for him.

''Tis a Christmas gift for thy brother Paul,' answered his mother, and she would have gone on to tell him how deadly a thing it was, had he given her time to speak. But her words fanned his fury into madness, for it seemed to him that this hated brother of his was claiming everything.

'Everything is for Paul! I am sick of his very name,' he cried. 'By my troth, he shall not have this!' and he snatched the vest from the table.

It was in vain that his mother and his aunt threw themselves at his feet, begging him to lay it down, and warning him that there was not a thread in it which was not poisoned. He paid no heed to their words, but rushed from the room, and, drawing it on, ran downstairs with a reckless laugh, to show the Lady Morna how fine he was.

Alas! alas! Scarce had he gained the hall than he fell to the ground in great pain.

Everyone crowded round him, and the two Countesses, terrified now by what they had done, tried in vain to tear the magic vest from his body. But he felt that it was too late, the deadly poison had done its work, and, waving them aside, he turned to his brother, who, in great distress, had knelt down and taken him tenderly in his arms.

'I wronged thee, Paul,' he gasped. 'For thou hast ever been true and kind. Forgive me in thy thoughts, and,' he added, gathering up his strength for one last effort, and pointing to the two wretched women who had wrought all this misery, '*beware of those two women*, for they seek to take thy life.' Then his head sank back on his brother's shoulder, and, with one long sigh, he died.

When he learned what had happened, and understood where the waistcoat came from, and for what purpose it had been intended, the anger of the Silent Earl knew no bounds. He swore a great oath that he would be avenged, not only on Snorro the Dwarf, but also on his wicked step-mother and her cruel sister.

His vengeance was baulked, however, for in the panic and confusion that followed Harold's death, the two Countesses slipped out of the Palace and fled to the coast, and took a boat in haste to Scotland, where they had great possessions, and where they were much looked up to, and where no one would believe a word against them.

But retribution fell on them in the end, as it always does fall, sooner or later, on everyone who is wicked, or selfish, or cruel; for the Norsemen invaded the land, and their Castle was set on fire, and they perished miserably in the flames.

When Earl Paul found that they had escaped, he set out in hot haste for the Island of Hoy, for he was determined that the Dwarf, at least, should not escape. But when he came to the Dwarfie Stone he found it silent and deserted, all trace of its uncanny occupants having disappeared.

No one knew what had become of them; a few people were inclined to think that the Dwarf and his Raven had accompanied the Countess Fraukirk and the Countess Helga on their flight, but the greater part of the Islanders held to the belief, which I think was the true one, that the Powers of the Air spirited Snorro away, and shut him up in some unknown place as a punishment for his wickedness, and that his Raven accompanied him.

At any rate, he was never seen again by any living person, and wherever he went, he lost all chance of finding the magic carbuncle.

As for the Silent Earl and his Irish Sweetheart, they were married as soon as Earl Harold's funeral was over; and for hundreds of years afterwards, when the inhabitants of the Orkney Isles wanted to express great happiness, they said, 'As happy as Earl Paul and the Countess Morna.'

THE LEGEND OF KNOCKGRAFTON

(IRISH)

There was once a poor man who lived in the fertile glen of Aherlow at the foot of the gloomy Galtee mountains, and he had a great hump on his back: he looked just as if his body had been rolled up and placed upon his shoulders; and his head was pressed down with the weight so much that his chin, when he was sitting, used to rest upon his knees for support. The country people were rather shy of meeting him in any lonesome place, for though, poor creature, he was as harmless and as inoffensive as a new-born infant, yet his deformity was so great that he scarcely appeared to be a human creature, and some ill-minded persons had set strange stories about him afloat. He was said to have a great knowledge of herbs and charms; but certain it was that he had a mighty skilful hand in plaiting straws and rushes into hats and baskets, which was the way he made his livelihood.

Lusmore, for that was the nickname put upon him by reason of his always wearing a sprig of the fairy cap, or lusmore (the foxglove), in his little straw hat, would ever get a higher penny for his plaited work than anyone else, and perhaps that was the reason why someone, out of envy, had circulated the strange stories about him. Be that as it may, it happened that he was returning one evening from the pretty town of Cahir toward Cappagh, and as little Lusmore walked very slowly, on account of the great hump upon his back, it was quite dark when he came to the old moat of Knockgrafton, which stood on the right-hand side of his road.

He was tired and weary, and in no ways comfortable in his own mind at thinking how much farther he had to travel, and that he should be walking all the night; so he sat down under the moat to rest himself, and began looking mournfully enough upon the moon, which,

> 'Rising in clouded majesty, at length
> Apparent Queen, unveiled her peerless light,
> And over the dark her silver mantle threw.'

Presently there arose a wild strain of unearthly melody upon the ear of little Lusmore; he listened, and he thought that he had never heard such ravishing music before. It was like the sound of many voices, each mingling and blending with the other so strangely that they seemed to be one, though all singing different strains, and the words of the song were these:

> 'Da Luan, Da Mort; Da Luan, Da Mort, Da Luan,
> Da Mort'

when there would be a moment's pause, and then the round of melody went on again.

Lusmore listened attentively, scarcely drawing his breath or else he might lose the slightest note. He now plainly perceived that the singing was within the moat; and though at first it had charmed him so much, he began to get tired of hearing the same round sung over and over so often without any change. So availing himself of the pause when Da Luan, Da Mort, had been sung three times, he took up the tune, and raised it with the words 'Augus Da Dardeen', and then went on singing with the voices inside of the moat, 'Da Luan, Da Mort', finishing the melody, when the pause again came, with 'Augus Da Dardeen'.

The fairies within Knockgrafton, for the song was a fairy melody, were so delighted the instant that they heard this additional tune that, it was determined to bring the mortal among them, whose musical skill so far exceeded theirs. Little Lusmore was conveyed into their company with the eddying speed of a whirlwind. Glorious to behold was the sight that burst upon him as he came down through the moat, twirling round and round, with the lightness of a straw, to the sweetest music that kept time to his motion. The greatest honour was then paid him, for he was put above all the musicians, and he had servants tending upon him, and everything to his heart's content. In short, he was made as much of as if he had been the first man in the land.

Presently Lusmore saw a great consultation going forward among the fairies, and, notwithstanding all their civility, he felt very much frightened, until one stepping out from the rest came up to him and said:

'Lusmore! Lusmore!
Doubt not, nor deplore,
For the hump which you bore
On your back is no more;
Look down on the floor,
And view it, Lusmore!'

When these words were said, poor little Lusmore felt himself so light, and so happy, that he thought he could have bounded at one jump over the moon, like the cow in the history of the cat and the fiddle; and he saw, with inexpressible pleasure, his hump tumble down upon the ground from his shoulders. He then tried to lift up his head, and he did so with caution, fearing that he might knock it against the ceiling of the grand hall, where he was; he looked round and round again with the greatest wonder and delight upon everything, which appeared more and more beautiful and overpowered at beholding such a resplendent scene. His head grew dizzy, and his eyesight became dim. At last he fell into a sound sleep, and when he awoke he found that it was broad daylight, the sun shining brightly, and the birds singing sweetly. He was lying just at the foot of the moat of Knockgrafton, with the cows and sheep grazing peaceably round about him. The first thing Lusmore did, after saying his prayers, was to put his hand behind to feel for his hump, but no sign of one was there on his back, and he looked at himself with great pride, for he had now become a well-shaped, dapper little fellow, and more than that, found himself in a full suit of new clothes, which he concluded the fairies had made for him.

Toward Cappagh he went, stepping out as lightly, and springing up at every step as if he had been all his life a dancing-master. Not a creature who met Lusmore knew him without his hump, and he had a great work to persuade everyone that he was the same man – in truth he was not, so far as the outward appearance went.

Of course it was not long before the story of Lusmore's hump got about, and a great wonder was made of it. Through the country, for miles round, it was the talk of everyone, high and low.

One morning, as Lusmore was sitting contented enough at his cabin door, up came an old woman to him, and asked him if he could direct her to Cappagh.

'I need give you no directions, my good woman,' said Lusmore, 'for this is Cappagh and whom may you want here?'

'I have come,' said the woman, 'out of Decie's country, in the county of Waterford, looking after one Lusmore, who, I have heard tell, had his hump taken off by the fairies. For there is a son of a gossip of mine who has got a hump on him that will be his death, and maybe, if he could use the same charm as Lusmore, the hump may be taken off him. And now I have told you the reason of my coming so far. It's to find out about this charm, if I can.'

Lusmore, who was ever a good-natured little fellow, told the woman all the particulars, how he had raised the tune for the fairies at Knockgrafton, how his hump had been removed from his shoulders, and how he had got a new suit of clothes into the bargain.

The woman thanked him very much, and then went away quite happy and easy in her own mind. When she came back to her gossip's house, in the county of Waterford, she told her everything that Lusmore had said, and they put the little humpbacked man, who was a peevish and cunning creature from his birth, upon a car, and took him all the way across the country. It was a long journey, but they did not care for that, so the hump was taken from off him. They brought him, just at nightfall, and left him under the old moat of Knockgrafton.

Jack Madden, for that was the humpy man's name, had not been sitting there long when he heard the tune going on within the moat much sweeter than before. For the fairies were singing it the way Lusmore had settled their music for them, and the song was going on, 'Da Luan, Da Mort, Da Luan, Da Mort, Da Luan, Da Mort, Augus Da Dardeen,' without ever stopping. Jack Madden,

THE LEGEND OF KNOCKGRAFTON

who was in a great hurry to get quit of his hump, never thought of waiting until the fairies had done, or watching for a fit opportunity to raise the tune higher again than Lusmore had. So having heard them sing it over seven times without stopping, out he bawls, never minding the time or the humour of the tune, or how he could bring his words in properly, 'Augus Da Dardeen, Augus Da Eena,' thinking that if one day was good, two were better. If Lusmore had one new suit of clothes given him, he should have two.

No sooner had the words passed his lips than he was taken up and whisked into the moat with prodigious force; and the fairies came crowding round about him with great anger, screeching and screaming, and roaring out:

'Who spoiled our tune? Who spoiled our tune?' and one stepped up to him above all the rest, and said:

'Jack Madden! Jack Madden!
Your words came so bad in
The tune we felt glad in;
This castle you're had in,
That your life we may sadden;
Here's two humps for Jack Madden!'

And 20 of the strongest fairies brought Lusmore's hump, and put it down upon poor Jack's back, over his own, where it became fixed as firmly as if it was nailed on with twelve-penny nails, by the best carpenter that ever drove one. Out of their castle they then kicked him; and in the morning, when Jack Madden's mother and her gossip came to look after their little man, they found him half dead, lying at the foot of the moat, with the other hump upon his back. Well to be sure, how they did look at each other! But they were afraid to say anything, lest a hump might be put upon their own shoulders. They brought the unlucky Jack Madden home with them, as downcast in their hearts and their looks as ever two gossips were. Through the weight of his other hump, and the long journey, he died soon after, leaving, they say, his heavy curse to anyone who would go to listen to fairy tunes again.

THE HEDGEHOG, THE JACKAL AND THE LION

(MOORISH)

Once upon a time the jackal went in search of the hedgehog and said to it, 'Come along. I know a garden of onions. We will fill our bellies.'

'How many tricks have you?' asked the hedgehog.

'I have a hundred and one.'

'And I,' said the other, 'have one and a half.'

They entered the garden and ate a good deal. The hedgehog ate a little and then went to see if he could get out of the entrance or not. When he had eaten enough so that he could just barely slip out, he stopped eating. As for the jackal, he never stopped eating until he was swollen very much.

As these things were going on, the owner of the garden arrived. The hedgehog saw him and said to his companion, 'Escape! The master is coming.' He himself took flight. But in spite of his exhortations, the jackal couldn't get through the opening. 'It is impossible,' he said.

'Where are those one hundred and one tricks? They don't serve you now.'

'May God have mercy on your parents, my uncle, lend me your half a trick.' 'Lie down on the ground,' answered the hedgehog. 'Play dead, shut your mouth, and stretch out your paws as if you were dead until the master of the garden shall see it and cast you into the street. Then you can run away.'

On that note, the hedgehog departed. The jackal lay down as he had told him until the owner of the garden came with his son and saw him lying as if dead. The child said to his father, 'Here is a dead jackal. He filled his belly with onions until he died.'

The man said, 'Go, drag him outside.'

'Yes,' said the child. He took him and stuck a thorn into him.

'Hold on, enough!' said the jackal. 'They play with reeds, but this is not sport.'

The child ran to his father and said, 'The jackal cried out, "A reed! a reed!"'

The father went and looked at the animal, which feigned death. 'Why do you tell me that it still lives?'

'It surely does.'

'Come away and leave that carrion.' The child stuck another thorn into the jackal, which cried, 'What, again?'

The child went to his father. 'He has just said, "What, again?"'

'Come now,' said the man, and he sent away his son. The latter took the jackal by the motionless tail and cast him into the street. Immediately the animal jumped up and started to run away. The child threw his slippers at him. The jackal took them, put them on, and departed.

On the way, he met the lion, who said, 'What is that footwear, my dear?'

'You don't know, my uncle? I am a shoemaker. My father, my uncle, my mother, my brother, my sister, and the little girl who was born at our house last night are all shoemakers.'

'Won't you make me a pair of shoes?' replied the lion.

'I will make you a pair. Bring me two fat camels. I will skin them and make you some good shoes.'

The lion went away and brought the two fat camels. 'They are thin,' said the jackal. 'Go change them for others.'

He brought two thin ones.

'They are fat,' said the jackal. He skinned them, cut some thorns from a palm-tree, rolled the leather around the lion's paws and fastened it there with the thorns.

'Ouch!' screamed the lion.

'He who wants to look finely ought not to say, "Ouch."'

'Enough, my dear.'

'My uncle, I will give you the rest of the slippers and boots.' He covered the lion's skin with the leather and stuck in the thorns. When he reached the knees, 'Enough, my dear,' said the lion. 'What kind of shoes are those?'

'Keep still, my uncle, these are slippers, boots, breeches, and clothes.'

When he came to the girdle the lion said, 'What kind of shoes are those?'

'My uncle, they are slippers, boots, breeches, and clothing.' In this way, he reached the lion's neck. 'Stay here,' he said, 'until the leather dries. When the sun rises look it in the face. When the moon rises, too, look it in the face.'

'It is good,' said the lion, and the jackal went away.

The lion remained and did as his companion had told him. But his feet began to swell, the leather became hard, and he could not get up. When the jackal came back he asked him, 'How are you, my uncle?'

'How am I? Wretch, son of a wretch, you have deceived me. Go, go. I will recommend you to my children.'

The jackal came near, and the lion seized him by the tail.

The jackal fled, leaving his tail in the lion's mouth.

'Now,' said the lion, 'you have no tail. When my feet get well I will catch you and eat you up.'

The jackal called his cousins and said to them, 'Let us go and fill our bellies with onions in a garden that I know.' They went with him. Arriving, he tied their tails to the branches of a young palm-tree and twisted them well. 'Who has tied our tails like this?' they asked. 'No one will come before you have filled your bellies. If you see the master of the garden approach, struggle and fly. You see that I, too, am bound as you are.' But he had tied an onion-stalk on himself. When the owner of the garden arrived, the jackal saw him coming. They struggled, their tails were all torn out, and stayed behind with the branches to which they were fastened. When the jackal saw the man, he cut the onion stem and escaped the first of all.

As for the lion, when his feet were cured, he went to take a walk and met his friend the jackal. He seized him and said, 'Now I've got you, son of a wretch.'

The other answered, 'What have I done, my uncle?'

'You stuck thorns in my flesh. You said to me, "I will make you some shoes." Now what shall I do to you?'

'It was not I,' said the jackal.

'It was you, and the proof is that you have your tail cut off.'

'But all my cousins are without tails, like me.'

'You lie, joker.'

'Let me call them and you will see.'

'Call them.'

At his call the jackals ran up, all without tails.

'Which of you is a shoemaker?' asked the lion.

'All of us,' they answered.

He said to them, 'I am going to bring you some red pepper. You shall eat of it, and the one who says, "Ouch!" that will be the one I'm looking for.'

'Go and get it.'

He brought them some red pepper, and they were going to eat it when the first jackal made a noise with his shoes, but he said to the lion, 'My uncle, I did not say, "Ouch!"' The lion sent them away, and they went about their business.

THE FALSE PRINCE AND THE TRUE

(PORTUGUESE)

The king had just awakened from his midday sleep, for it was summer, and everyone rose early and rested from twelve to three, as they do in hot countries. He had dressed himself in cool white clothes, and was passing through the hall on his way to the council chamber, when a number of young nobles suddenly appeared before him, and one amongst them stepped forward and spoke.

'Sire, this morning we were all playing tennis in the court, the prince and this gentleman with the rest, when there broke out some dispute about the game. The prince lost his temper, and said many insulting things to the other, who was playing against him, till at length the gentleman whom you see there struck him violently in the face, so that the blood ran from his mouth and nose. We were all so horrified at the sight, that we should most likely have killed the man then and there, for daring to lay hands on the prince, had not his grandfather the duke stepped between and commanded us to lay the affair before you.'

The king had listened attentively to the story, and when it was ended he said:

'I suppose the prince had no arms with him, or else he would have used them?'

'Yes, sire, he had arms; he always carries a dagger in his belt. But when he saw the blood pouring from his face, he went to a corner of the court and began to cry, which was the strangest thing of all.'

On hearing this the king walked to the window and stood for a few minutes with his back to the room, where the company of young men remained silent. Then he came back, his face white and stern.

'I tell you,' he said, 'and it is the solemn truth, that I would rather you had told me that the prince was dead, though he is my only son, than know that he would suffer such an injury without attempting to avenge it. As for the gentleman who struck him, he will be brought before my judges, and will plead his own cause, but I hardly think he can escape death, after having assaulted the heir to the crown.'

The young man raised his head as if to reply, but the king would not listen, and commanded his guards to put him under arrest, adding, however, that if the prisoner wished to visit any part of the city, he was at liberty to do so properly guarded, and in 15 days he would be brought to trial before the highest judges in the land.

The young man left the king's presence, surrounded by soldiers, and accompanied by many of his friends, for he was a great favourite. By their advice he spent the 14 days that remained to him going about to seek counsel from wise men of all sorts, as to how he might escape death, but no one could help him, for none could find any excuse for the blow he had given to the prince.

The 14th night had come, and in despair the prisoner went out to take his last walk through the city. He wandered on hardly knowing where he went, and his face was so white and desperate that none of his companions dared speak to him. The sad little procession had passed some hours in this manner, when, near the gate of a monastery, an old woman appeared round a corner, and suddenly stood before the young man. She was bent almost double, and was so wizened and wrinkled that she looked at least 90; only her eyes were bright and quick as those of a girl.

'Sir,' she said, 'I know all that has happened to you, and how you are seeking if in any way you can save your life. But there is none that can answer that question save only I myself, if you will promise to do all I ask.'

At her words the prisoner felt as if a load had all at once been rolled off him.

'Oh, save me, and I will do anything!' he cried. 'It is so hard to leave the world and go out into the darkness.'

'You will not need to do that,' answered the old woman, 'you have only got to marry me, and you will soon be free.'

'Marry you?' exclaimed he, 'but – but – I am not yet 20, and you – why, you must be 100 at least! Oh, no, it is quite impossible.'

He spoke without thinking, but the flash of anger which darted from her eyes made him feel uncomfortable. However, all she said was:

'As you like; since you reject me, let the crows have you,' and hurried away down the street.

Left to himself, the full horror of his coming death rushed upon the young man, and he understood that he had thrown away his sole chance of life. Well, if he must, he must, he said to himself, and began to run as fast as he could after the old crone, who by this time could scarcely be seen, even in the moonlight. Who would have believed a woman past 90 could walk with such speed? It seemed more like flying! But at length, breathless and exhausted, he reached her side, and gasped out:

'Madam, pardon me for my hasty words just now; I was wrong, and will thankfully accept the offer you made me.'

'Ah, I thought you would come to your senses,' answered she, in rather an odd voice. 'We have no time to lose – follow me at once,' and they went on silently and swiftly till they stopped at the door of a small house in which the priest lived. Before him the old woman bade the prisoner swear that she should be his wife, and this he did in the presence of witnesses. Then, begging the priest and the guards to leave them alone for a little, she told the young man what he was to do, when the next morning he was brought before the king and the judges.

The hall was full to overflowing when the prisoner entered it, and all marvelled at the brightness of his face. The king inquired if he had any excuse to plead for the high treason he had committed by striking the heir to the throne, and, if so, to be quick in setting it forth. With a low bow the youth made answer in a clear voice:

'O my lord and gracious king, and you, nobles and wise men of the land, I leave my cause without fear in your hands, knowing that you will listen and judge rightly, and that you will suffer me to speak to the end, before you give judgment.

'For four years, you, O king, had been married to the queen and yet had no children, which grieved you greatly. The queen saw this, and likewise that your love was going from her, and thought night and day of some plan that might put an end to this evil. At length, when you were away fighting in distant countries, she decided what she would do, and adopted in secret the baby of a poor quarryman, sending a messenger to tell you that you had a son. No one suspected the truth except a priest to whom the queen confessed the truth, and in a few weeks she fell ill and died, leaving the baby to be brought up as became a prince. And now, if your highness will permit me, I will speak of myself.'

'What you have already told me,' answered the king, 'is so strange that I cannot imagine what more there is to tell, but go on with your story.'

'One day, shortly after the death of the queen,' continued the young man, 'your highness was hunting, and outstripped all your attendants while chasing the deer. You were in a part of the country which you did not know, so seeing an orchard all pink and white with apple-blossoms, and a girl tossing a ball in one corner, you went up to her to ask your way. But when she turned to answer you, you were so struck with her beauty that all else fled from your mind. Again and again you rode back to see her, and at length persuaded her to marry you. She only thought you a poor knight, and agreed that as you wished it, the marriage should be kept secret.

'After the ceremony you gave her three rings and a charm with a cross on it, and then put her in a cottage in the forest, thinking to hide the matter securely.

'For some months you visited the cottage every week; but a rebellion broke out in a distant part of the kingdom, and called for your presence. When next you rode up to the cottage, it was empty, and none could inform you whither your bride had gone. That, sire, I can now tell you,' and the young man paused and looked at the king, who coloured deeply. 'She went back to her father the old duke, once your chamberlain, and the cross on her breast revealed at once who you were. Fierce was his anger when he heard his daughter's tale, and he vowed that he would hide her safely from you, till the day when you would claim her publicly as your queen.

'By and bye I was born, and was brought up by my grandfather in one of his great houses. Here are the rings you gave to my mother, and here is the cross, and these will prove if I am your son or not.'

As he spoke the young man laid the jewels at the feet of the king, and the nobles and the judges pressed round to examine them. The king alone did not move from his seat, for he had forgotten the hall of justice and all about him, and saw only the apple-orchard, as it was 20 years ago, and the beautiful girl playing at ball. A sudden silence round him made him look up, and he found the eyes of the assembly fixed on him.

'It is true; it is he who is my son, and not the other,' he said with an effort, 'and let every man present swear to acknowledge him as king, after my death.'

Therefore one by one they all knelt before him and took the oath, and a message was sent to the false prince, forbidding him ever again to appear at court, though a handsome pension was granted him.

At last the ceremony was over, and the king, signing to his newly found son to follow him, rose and went into another room.

'Tell me how you knew all that,' he said, throwing himself into a carved chair filled with crimson cushions, and the prince told of his meeting with the old woman who had brought him the jewels from his mother, and how he had sworn before a priest to marry her, though he did not want to do it, on account of the difference in their ages, and besides, he would rather receive a bride chosen by the king himself. But the king frowned, and answered sharply:

'You swore to marry her if she saved your life, and, come what may, you must fulfil your promise.' Then, striking a silver shield that hung close by, he said to the equerry who appeared immediately:

'Go and seek the priest who lives near the door of the prison, and ask him where you can find the old woman who visited him last night; and when you have found her, bring her to the palace.'

It took some time to discover the whereabouts of the old woman, but at length it was accomplished, and when she arrived at the palace with the equerry, she was received with royal honours, and became the bride of the prince. The guards looked at each other with astonished eyes, as the wizened creature, bowed with age, passed between their lines; but they were more amazed still at the lightness of her step as she skipped up the steps to the great door before which the king was standing, with the prince at his side. If they both felt a shock at the appearance of the aged lady they did not show it, and the king, with a grave bow, took her hand, and led her to the chapel, where a bishop was waiting to perform the marriage ceremony.

For the next few weeks little was seen of the prince, who spent all his days in hunting, and trying to forget the old wife at home. As for the princess, no one troubled himself about her, and she passed the days alone in her apartments, for she had absolutely declined the services of the ladies-in-waiting whom the king had appointed for her.

One night the prince returned after a longer chase than usual, and he was so tired that he went up straight to bed. Suddenly he was awakened by a strange noise in the room, and suspecting that a robber might have stolen in, he jumped out of bed, and seized his sword, which lay ready to his hand. Then he perceived that the noise proceeded from the next room, which belonged to the princess, and was lighted by a burning torch. Creeping softly to the door, he peeped through it, and beheld her lying quietly, with a crown of gold and pearls upon her head, her wrinkles all gone, and her face, which was whiter than the snow, as fresh as that of a girl of 14. Could that really be his wife – that beautiful, beautiful creature?

THE FALSE PRINCE AND THE TRUE

The prince was still gazing in surprise when the lady opened her eyes and smiled at him.

'Yes, I really am your wife,' she said, as if she had guessed his thoughts, 'and the enchantment is ended. Now I must tell you who I am, and what befell to cause me to take the shape of an old woman.

'The king of Granada is my father, and I was born in the palace which overlooks the plain of the Vega. I was only a few months old when a wicked fairy, who had a spite against my parents, cast a spell over me, bending my back and wrinkling my skin till I looked as if I was 100 years old, and making me such an object of disgust to everyone, that at length the king ordered my nurse to take me away from the palace. She was the only person who cared about me, and we lived together in this city on a small pension allowed me by the king.

'When I was about three an old man arrived at our house, and begged my nurse to let him come in and rest, as he could walk no longer. She saw that he was very ill, so put him to bed and took such care of him that by and bye he was as strong as ever. In gratitude for her goodness to him, he told her that he was a wizard and could give her anything she chose to ask for, except life or death, so she answered that what she longed for most in the world was that my wrinkled skin should disappear, and that I should regain the beauty with which I was born. To this he replied that as my misfortune resulted from a spell, this was rather difficult, but he would do his best, and at any rate he could promise that before my 15th birthday I should be freed from the enchantment if I could get a man who would swear to marry me as I was.

'As you may suppose, this was not easy, as my ugliness was such that no one would look at me a second time. My nurse and

I were almost in despair, as my 15th birthday was drawing near, and I had never so much as spoken to a man. At last we received a visit from the wizard, who told us what had happened at court, and your story, bidding me to put myself in your way when you had lost all hope, and offer to save you if you would consent to marry me.

'That is my history, and now you must beg the king to send messengers at once to Granada, to inform my father of our marriage, and I think,' she added with a smile, 'that he will not refuse us his blessing.'

CROCODILE'S TREASON

(SOUTH AFRICAN)

Crocodile was, in the days when animals still could talk, the acknowledged foreman of all water creatures and if one should judge from appearances one would say that he still is. But in those days it was his especial duty to have a general care of all water animals, and when one year it was exceedingly dry, and the water of the river where they had lived dried up and became scarce, he was forced to make a plan to trek over to another river a short distance from there.

He first sent Otter out to spy. He stayed away two days and brought back a report that there was still good water in the other river, real sea-cow holes, that not even a drought of several years could dry up.

After he had ascertained this, Crocodile called to his side Tortoise and Alligator.

'Look here,' said he, 'I need you two to-night to carry a report to Lion. So then get ready; the veldt is dry, and you will probably have to travel for a few days without any water. We must make peace with Lion and his subjects, otherwise we utterly perish this year. And he must help us to trek over to the other river, especially past the Boer's farm that lies in between, and to travel unmolested by any of the animals of the veldt, so long as the trek lasts. A fish on land is sometimes a very helpless thing, as you all know.' The two had it mighty hard in the burning sun, and on the dry veldt, but eventually they reached Lion and handed him the treaty.

'What is going on now?' thought Lion to himself, when he had read it. 'I must consult Jackal first,' said he. But to the commissioners he gave back an answer that he would be the following evening with his advisers at the appointed place, at the big vaarland willow tree, at the farther end of the hole of water, where Crocodile had his headquarters.

When Tortoise and Alligator came back, Crocodile was exceedingly pleased with himself at the turn the case had taken.

He allowed Otter and a few others to be present and ordered them on that evening to have ready plenty of fish and other eatables for their guests under the vaarland willow.

That evening as it grew dark Lion appeared with Wolf, Jackal, Baboon, and a few other important animals, at the appointed place, and they were received in the most open-hearted manner by Crocodile and the other water creatures.

Crocodile was so glad at the meeting of the animals that he now and then let fall a great tear of joy that disappeared into the sand. After the other animals had done well by the fish, Crocodile laid bare to them the condition of affairs and opened up his plan. He wanted only peace among all animals; for they not only destroyed one another, but the Boer, too, would in time destroy them all.

The Boer had already stationed at the source of the river no less than three steam pumps to irrigate his land, and the water was becoming scarcer every day. More than this, he took advantage of their unfortunate position by making them sit in the shallow water and then, one after the other, bringing about their death. As Lion was, on this account, inclined to make peace, it was to his glory to take this opportunity and give his hand to these peace-making water creatures, and carry out their part of the contract, namely, escort them from the dried-up water, past the Boer's farm and to the long sea-cow pools.

'And what benefit shall we receive from it?' asked Jackal.

'Well,' answered Crocodile, 'the peace made is of great benefit to both sides. We will not exterminate each other. If you desire to come and drink water, you can do so with an easy mind, and not be the least bit nervous that I, or any one of us will seize you by the nose; and so also with all the other animals. And from your side we are to be freed from Elephant, who has the habit, whenever he gets the opportunity, of tossing us with his trunk up into some open and narrow fork of a tree and there allowing us to become biltong.'

Lion and Jackal stepped aside to consult with one another, and then Lion wanted to know what form of security he would have that Crocodile would keep to his part of the contract.

'I stake my word of honour,' was the prompt answer from Crocodile, and he let drop a few more long tears of honesty into the sand.

Baboon then said it was all square and honest as far as he could see into the case. He thought it was nonsense to attempt to dig pitfalls for one another; because he personally was well aware that his race would benefit somewhat from this contract of peace and friendship. And more than this, they must consider that use must be made of the fast disappearing water, for even in the best of times it was an unpleasant thing to be always carrying your life about in your hands. He would, however, like to suggest to the King that it would be well to have everything put down in writing, so that there would be nothing to regret in case it was needed.

Jackal did not want to listen to the agreement. He could not see that it would benefit the animals of the veldt. But Wolf, who had fully satisfied himself with the fish, was in an exceptionally peace-loving mood, and he advised Lion again to close the agreement.

After Lion had listened to all his advisers, and also the pleading tones of Crocodile's followers, he held forth in a speech in which he said that he was inclined to enter into the agreement, seeing that it was clear that Crocodile and his subjects were in a very tight place.

There and then a document was drawn up, and it was resolved, before midnight, to begin the trek. Crocodile's messengers swam in all directions to summon together the water animals for the trek.

Frogs croaked and crickets chirped in the long water grass. It was not long before all the animals had assembled at the vaarland willow. In the meantime Lion had sent out a few despatch riders to his subjects to raise a commando for an escort, and long ere midnight these also were at the vaarland willow in the moonlight.

The trek then was regulated by Lion and Jackal. Jackal was to take the lead to act as spy, and when he was able to draw Lion to one side, he said to him:

'See here, I do not trust this affair one bit, and I want to tell you straight out, I am going to make tracks! I will spy for you until you reach the sea-cow pool, but I am not going to be the one to await your arrival there.'

Elephant had to act as advance guard because he could walk so softly and could hear and smell so well. Then came Lion with one division of the animals, then Crocodile's trek with a flank protection of both sides, and Wolf received orders to bring up the rear.

Meanwhile, while all this was being arranged, Crocodile was smoothly preparing his treason. He called Yellow Snake to one side and said to him: 'It is to our advantage to have these animals, who go among us every day, and who will continue to do so, fall into the hands of the Boer. Listen, now! You remain behind unnoticed, and when you hear me shout you will know that we have arrived safely at the sea-cow pool. Then you must harass the Boer's dogs as much as you can, and the rest will look out for themselves.'

Thereupon the trek moved on. It was necessary to go very slowly as many of the water animals were not accustomed to the journey on land; but they trekked past the Boer's farm in safety, and toward break of day they were all safely at the sea-cow pool. There most of the water animals disappeared suddenly into the deep water, and Crocodile also began to make preparations to follow their example. With tearful eyes he said to Lion that he was, oh, so thankful for the help, that, from pure relief and joy, he must first give vent to his feelings by a few screams. Thereupon he suited his words to actions so that even the mountains echoed, and then thanked Lion on behalf of his subjects, and purposely continued with a long speech, dwelling on all the benefits both sides would derive from the agreement of peace.

Lion was just about to say good day and take his departure, when the first shot fell, and with it Elephant and a few other animals.

'I told you all so!' shouted Jackal from the other side of the sea-cow pool. 'Why did you allow yourselves to be misled by a few Crocodile tears?'

Crocodile had disappeared long ago into the water. All one saw was just a lot of bubbles; and on the banks there was an actual war against the animals. It simply crackled the way the Boers shot them.

But most of them, fortunately, came out of it alive.

Shortly after, they say, Crocodile received his well-earned reward, when he met a driver with a load of dynamite. And even now when the Elephant gets the chance he pitches them up into the highest forks of the trees.

ELEPHANT AND TORTOISE

(NAMIBIAN)

Two powers, Elephant and Rain, had a dispute. Elephant said, 'If you say that you nourish me, in what way is it that you do so?' Rain answered, 'If you say that I do not nourish you, when I go away, will you not die?' And Rain then departed.

Elephant said, 'Vulture! Cast lots to make rain for me.'

Vulture said, 'I will not cast lots.' Then Elephant said to Crow, 'Cast lots!' who answered, 'Give the things with which I may cast lots.' Crow cast lots and rain fell. It rained at the lagoons, but they dried up and only one lagoon remained.

Elephant went a-hunting. There was, however, Tortoise, to whom Elephant said, 'Tortoise, remain at the water!' Thus Tortoise was left behind when Elephant went a-hunting.

There came Giraffe, and it said to Tortoise, 'Give me water!' Tortoise answered, 'The water belongs to Elephant.'

There came Zebra, who said to Tortoise, 'Give me water!' Tortoise answered, 'The water belongs to Elephant.'

There came Gemsbok, and it said to Tortoise, 'Give me water!' Tortoise answered, 'The water belongs to Elephant.'

There came Wildebeest, and it said, 'Give me water!' Tortoise said, 'The water belongs to Elephant.'

There came Roodebok, and it said to Tortoise, 'Give me water!' Tortoise answered, 'The water belongs to Elephant.'

There came Springbok, and it said to Tortoise, 'Give me water!' Tortoise said, 'The water belongs to Elephant.'

There came Jackal, and it said to Tortoise, 'Give me water!' Tortoise said, 'The water belongs to Elephant.'

There came Lion, and it said, 'Little Tortoise, give me water!' When little Tortoise was about to say something, Lion got hold of him and beat him. Lion drank of the water, and since then the animals drink water.

When Elephant came back from the hunting, he said, 'Little Tortoise, is there water?' Tortoise answered, 'The animals have drunk the water.' Elephant asked, 'Little Tortoise, shall I chew you or swallow you down?' Little Tortoise said, 'Swallow me, if you please!' And Elephant swallowed him whole.

After Elephant had swallowed Little Tortoise, and he had entered his body, he tore off his liver, heart, and kidneys. Elephant said, 'Little Tortoise, you kill me.'

So Elephant died; but little Tortoise came out of his dead body, and went wherever he liked.

THUNDER AND ANANSI

(WEST AFRICAN)

There had been a long and severe famine in the land where Anansi lived. He had been quite unable to obtain food for his poor wife and family. One day, gazing desperately out to sea, he saw, rising from the midst of the water, a tiny island with a tall palm-tree upon it. He determined to reach this tree – if any means proved possible – and climb it, in the hope of finding a few nuts to reward him. How to get there was the difficulty.

This, however, solved itself when he reached the beach, for there lay the means to his hand, in the shape of an old broken boat. It certainly did not look very strong, but Anansi decided to try it.

His first six attempts were unsuccessful – a great wave dashed him back on the beach each time he tried to put off. He was persevering, however, and at the seventh trial was successful in getting away. He steered the battered old boat as best he could, and at length reached the palm-tree of his desire. Having tied the boat to the trunk of the tree – which grew almost straight out of the water – he climbed toward the nuts. Plucking all he could reach, he dropped them, one by one, down to the boat. To his dismay, every one missed the boat and fell, instead, into the water until only the last one remained. This he aimed even more carefully than the others, but it also fell into the water and disappeared from his hungry eyes. He had not tasted even one and now all were gone.

He could not bear the thought of going home empty-handed, so, in his despair, he threw himself into the water, too. To his complete astonishment, instead of being drowned, he found himself standing on the sea-bottom in front of a pretty little cottage. From the latter came an old man, who asked Anansi what he wanted so badly that he had come to Thunder's cottage to seek it. Anansi told his tale of woe, and Thunder showed himself most sympathetic.

He went into the cottage and fetched a fine cooking-pot, which he presented to Anansi – telling him that he need never be hungry again. The pot would always supply enough food for himself and his family. Anansi was most grateful, and left Thunder with many thanks.

Being anxious to test the pot at once, Anansi only waited till he was again seated in the old boat to say, 'Pot, pot, what you used to do for your master do now for me.' Immediately good food of all sorts appeared. Anansi ate a hearty meal, which he very much enjoyed.

On reaching land again, his first thought was to run home and give all his family a good meal from his wonderful pot. A selfish, greedy fear prevented him. 'What if I should use up all the magic of the pot on them, and have nothing more left for myself! Better keep the pot a secret – then I can enjoy a meal when I want one.' So, his mind full of this thought, he hid the pot.

He reached home, pretending to be utterly worn out with fatigue and hunger. There was not a grain of food to be had anywhere. His wife and poor children were weak with want of it, but selfish Anansi took no notice of that. He congratulated himself at the thought of his magic pot, now safely hidden in his room. There he retired from time to time when he felt hungry, and enjoyed a good meal. His family got thinner and thinner, but he grew plumper and plumper. They began to suspect some secret, and determined to find it out. His eldest son, Kweku Tsin, had the power of changing himself into any shape he chose; so he took the form of a tiny fly, and accompanied his father everywhere. At last, Anansi, feeling hungry, entered his room and closed the door. Next he took the pot, and had a fine meal. Having replaced the pot in its hiding-place, he went out, on the pretence of looking for food.

As soon as he was safely out of sight, Kweku Tsin fetched out the pot and called all his hungry family to come at once. They had as good a meal as their father had had. When they had finished, Mrs Anansi – to punish her husband – said she would take the pot down to the village and give everybody a meal. This she did – but alas! in working to prepare so much food at one time, the pot grew too hot and melted away. What was to be done now? Anansi would be so angry! His wife forbade everyone to mention the pot.

Anansi returned, ready for his supper, and, as usual, went into his room, carefully shutting the door. He went to the hiding-place – it was empty! He looked around in consternation. No pot was to be seen anywhere. Someone must have discovered it. His family must be the culprits; he would find a means to punish them.

Saying nothing to anyone about the matter, he waited till morning. As soon as it was light he started off towards the shore, where the old boat lay. Getting into the boat, it started of its own accord and glided swiftly over the water – straight for the palm-tree. When he arrived there, Anansi attached the boat as before and climbed the tree. This time, unlike the last, the nuts almost fell into his hands. When he aimed them at the boat they fell easily into it – not one, as before, dropping into the water. He deliberately took them and threw them overboard, immediately jumping after them. As before, he found himself in front of Thunder's cottage, with Thunder waiting to hear his tale. This he told, the old man showing the same sympathy as he had previously done.

This time, however, he presented Anansi with a fine stick and bade him good-bye. Anansi could scarcely wait till he got into the boat – so anxious was he to try the magic properties of his new gift.

'Stick, stick,' he said, 'what you used to do for your master do for me also.' The stick began to beat him so severely that, in a few minutes, he was obliged to jump into the water and swim ashore, leaving boat and stick to drift away where they pleased. Then he returned sorrowfully homeward, bemoaning his many bruises and wishing he had acted more wisely from the beginning.

HOW THE BRAZILIAN BEETLES GOT THEIR GORGEOUS COATS

(BRAZILIAN)

In Brazil the beetles have such beautifully coloured, hard-shelled coats upon their backs that they are often set in pins and necklaces like precious stones. Once upon a time, years and years ago, they had ordinary plain brown coats. This is how it happened that the Brazilian beetle earned a new coat.

One day a little brown beetle was crawling along a wall when a big grey rat ran out of a hole in the wall and looked down scornfully at the little beetle. 'O ho!' he said to the beetle, 'how slowly you crawl along. You'll never get anywhere in the world. Just look at me and see how fast I can run.'

The big grey rat ran to the end of the wall, wheeled around, and came back to the place where the little beetle was slowly crawling along at only a tiny distance from where the rat had left her.

'Don't you wish that you could run like that?' said the big grey rat to the little brown beetle.

'You are surely a fast runner,' replied the little brown beetle politely. Her mother had taught her always to be polite and had often said to her that a really polite beetle never boasts about her own accomplishments. The little brown beetle never boasted a single boast about the things she could do. She just went on slowly crawling along the wall.

A bright green and gold parrot in the mango tree over the wall had heard the conversation. 'How would you like to race with the beetle?' he asked the big grey rat. 'I live next door to the tailor bird,' he added, 'and just to make the race exciting I'll offer a bright coloured coat as a prize to the one who wins the race. You may choose for it any colour you like and I'll have it made to order.'

'I'd like a yellow coat with stripes like the tiger's,' said the big grey rat, looking over his shoulder at his gaunt grey sides as if he were already admiring his new coat.

'I'd like a beautiful, bright coloured new coat, too,' said the little brown beetle.

The big grey rat laughed long and loud until his gaunt grey sides were shaking. 'Why, you talk just as if you thought you had a chance to win the race,' he said, when he could speak.

The bright green and gold parrot set the royal palm tree at the top of the cliff as the goal of the race. He gave the signal to start and then he flew away to the royal palm tree to watch for the end of the race.

The big grey rat ran as fast as he could. Then he thought how very tired he was getting. 'What's the use of hurrying?' he said to himself. 'The little brown beetle can not possibly win. If I were racing with somebody who could really run it would be very different.' Then he started to run more slowly but every time his heart beat it said, 'Hurry up! Hurry up!' The big grey rat decided that it was best to obey the little voice in his heart so he hurried just as fast as he could.

When he reached the royal palm tree at the top of the cliff he could hardly believe his eyes. He thought he must be having a bad dream. There was the little brown beetle sitting quietly beside the bright green and gold parrot. The big grey rat had never been so surprised in all his life. 'How did you ever manage to run fast enough to get here so soon?' he asked the little brown beetle as soon as he could catch his breath.

The little brown beetle drew out the tiny wings from her sides. 'Nobody said anything about having to run to win the race,' she replied, 'so I flew instead.'

'I did not know that you could fly,' said the big grey rat in a subdued little voice.

'After this,' said the bright green and gold parrot, 'never judge anyone by his looks alone. You never can tell how often or where you may find concealed wings. You have lost the prize.'

Until this day, even in Brazil where the flowers and birds and beasts and insects have such gorgeous colouring, the rat wears a plain dull grey coat.

Then the parrot turned to the little brown beetle who was waiting quietly at his side. 'What colour do you want your new coat to be?' he asked.

The little brown beetle looked up at the bright green and gold parrot, at the green and gold palm trees above their heads, at the green mangoes with golden flushes on their cheeks lying on the ground under the mango trees, at the golden sunshine upon the distant green hills. 'I choose a coat of green and gold,' she said.

From that day to this the Brazilian beetle has worn a coat of green with golden lights upon it.

For years and years the Brazilian beetles were all very proud to wear green and gold coats like that of the beetle who raced with the rat.

Then, once upon a time, it happened that there was a little beetle who grew discontented with her coat of green and gold.

She looked up at the blue sky and out at the blue sea and wished that she had a blue coat instead. She talked about it so much that finally her mother took her to the parrot who lived next to the tailor bird.

'You may change your coat for a blue one,' said the parrot, 'but if you change you'll have to give up something.'

'Oh, I'll gladly give up anything if only I may have a blue coat instead of a green and gold one,' said the discontented little beetle.

When she received her new coat she thought it was very beautiful. It was a lovely shade of blue and it had silvery white lights upon it like the light of the stars. When she put it on, however, she discovered that it was not hard like the green and gold one. From that day to this the blue beetles' coats have not been hard and firm. That is the reason why the jewellers have difficulty in using them in pins and necklaces like other beetles.

From the moment that the little beetle put on her new blue coat she never grew again. From that day to this the blue beetles have been much smaller than the green and gold ones.

When the Brazilians made their flag they took for it a square of green the colour of the green beetle's coat. Within this square they placed a diamond of gold like the golden lights which play upon the green beetle's back. Then, within the diamond, they drew a circle to represent the round earth and they coloured it blue like the coat of the blue beetle. Upon the blue circle they placed stars of silvery white like the silvery white lights on the back of the blue beetle. About the blue circle of the earth which they thus pictured they drew a band of white, and upon this band they wrote the motto of their country, '*Ordem e Progresso*, order and progress.'

PAUPPUKKEEWIS

(NATIVE AMERICAN)

A man of large stature and great activity of mind and body found himself standing alone on a prairie. He thought to himself:

'How came I here? Are there no beings on this earth but myself? I must travel and see. I must walk till I find the abodes of men.'

So as soon as his mind was made up he set out, he knew not whither, in search of habitations. No obstacles diverted him from his purpose. Prairies, rivers, woods, and storms did not daunt his courage or turn him back. After travelling a long time he came to a wood in which he saw decayed stumps of trees, as if they had been cut in ancient times, but he found no other traces of men. Pursuing his journey he found more recent marks of the same kind, and later on he came to fresh traces of human beings, first their footsteps, and then the wood they had cut lying in heaps.

Continuing on he emerged towards dusk from the forest, and beheld at a distance a large village of high lodges, standing on rising ground. He said to himself:

'I will arrive there at a run.'

Off he started with all his speed, and on coming to the first lodge he jumped over it. Those within saw something pass over the top, and then they heard a thump on the ground.

'What is that?' they all said.

One came out to see, and, finding a stranger, invited him in. He found himself in the presence of an old chief and several men who were seated in the lodge. Meat was set before him, after which the chief asked him where he was going and what his name was. He answered he was in search of adventures, and that his name was Pauppukkeewis (grasshopper). The eyes of all were fixed upon him.

'Pauppukkeewis!' said one to another, and the laugh went round.

Pauppukkeewis made but a short stay in the village. He was not easy there. The place gave him no opportunity to display his powers.

'I will be off,' he said, and taking with him a young man who had formed a strong attachment for him and who might serve him as a mesh-in-au-wa (official who bears the pipe), he set out once more on his travels. The two travelled together, and when the young man was fatigued with walking Pauppukkeewis would show him a few tricks, such as leaping over trees, and turning round on one leg till he made the dust fly in a cloud around him. In this manner he very much amused his companion, though at times his performance somewhat alarmed him.

One day they came to a large village, where they were well received. The people told them that there were a number of manitoes who lived some distance away and who killed all who came to their lodge.

The people had made many attempts to extirpate these manitoes, but the war parties that went out for this purpose were always unsuccessful.

'I will go and see them,' said Pauppukkeewis.

The chief of the village warned him of the danger he would run, but finding him resolved, said:

'Well, if you will go, since you are my guest, I will send 20 warriors with you.'

Pauppukkeewis thanked him for this. Twenty young men offered themselves for the expedition. They went forward, and in a short time descried the lodge of the manitoes. Pauppukkeewis placed his friend and the warriors near him so that they might see all that passed, and then he went alone into the lodge. When he entered he found five horrible-looking manitoes eating. These were the father and four sons. Their appearance was hideous. Their eyes were set low in their heads as if the manitoes were half starved. They offered Pauppukkeewis part of their meat, but he refused it.

'What have you come for?' asked the old one.

'Nothing,' answered Pauppukkeewis.

At this they all stared at him.

'Do you not wish to wrestle?' they all asked.

'Yes,' replied he.

A hideous smile passed over their faces.

'You go,' said the others to their eldest brother.

Pauppukkeewis and his antagonist were soon clinched in each other's arms. He knew the manitoes' object – they wanted his flesh – but he was prepared for them.

'Haw, haw!' they cried, and the dust and dry leaves flew about the wrestlers as if driven by a strong wind.

The manito was strong, but Pauppukkeewis soon found he could master him. He tripped him up, and threw him with a giant's force head foremost on a stone, and he fell insensible.

The brothers stepped up in quick succession, but Pauppukkeewis put his tricks in full play, and soon all the four lay bleeding on the ground. The old manito got frightened, and ran for his life.

Pauppukkeewis pursued him for sport. Sometimes he was before him, sometimes over his head. Now he would give him a kick, now a push, now a trip, till the manito was quite exhausted. Meanwhile Pauppukkeewis's friend and the warriors came up, crying:

'Ha, ha, a! Ha, ha, a! Pauppukkeewis is driving him before him.'

At length Pauppukkeewis threw the manito to the ground with such force that he lay senseless, and the warriors, carrying him off, laid him with the bodies of his sons, and set fire to the whole, consuming them to ashes.

Around the lodge Pauppukkeewis and his friends saw a large number of bones, the remains of the warriors whom the manitoes had slain. Taking three arrows, Pauppukkeewis called upon the Great Spirit, and then, shooting an arrow in the air, he cried:

'You, who are lying down, rise up, or you will be hit.'

The bones at these words all collected in one place. Again Pauppukkeewis shot another arrow into the air, crying:

'You, who are lying down, rise up, or you will be hit,' and each bone drew towards its fellow.

Then he shot a third arrow, crying:

'You, who are lying down, rise up, or you will be hit,' and the bones immediately came together, flesh came over them, and the warriors, whose remains they were, stood before Pauppukkeewis alive and well.

He led them to the chief of the village, who had been his friend, and gave them up to him. Soon after, the chief with his counsellors came to him, saying:

'Who is more worthy to rule than you? You alone can defend us.'

Pauppukkeewis thanked the chief, but told him he must set out again in search of further adventures. The chief and the counsellors pressed him to remain, but he was resolved to leave them, and so he told the chief to make his friend ruler while he himself went on his travels.

'I will come again,' said he, 'sometime and see you.'

'Ho, ho, ho!' they all cried, 'come back again and see us.'

He promised that he would, and set out alone.

After travelling for some time, he came to a large lake, and on looking about he saw an enormous otter on an island. He thought to himself:

'His skin will make me a fine pouch,' and, drawing near, he drove an arrow into the otter's side. He waded into the lake, and with some difficulty dragged the carcass ashore. He took out the entrails, but even then the carcass was so heavy that it was as much as he could do to drag it up a hill overlooking the lake. As soon as he got it into the sunshine, where it was warm, he skinned the otter, and threw the carcass away, for he said to himself:

'The war-eagle will come, and then I shall have a chance to get his skin and his feathers to put on my head.'

Very soon he heard a noise in the air, but he could see nothing. At length a large eagle dropped, as if from the sky, on to the otter's carcass. Pauppukkeewis drew his bow and sent an arrow through the bird's body. The eagle made a dying effort and lifted the carcass up several feet, but it could not disengage its claws, and the weight soon brought the bird down again.

Then Pauppukkeewis skinned the bird, crowned his head with its feathers, and set out again on his journey.

After walking a while he came to a lake, the water of which came right up to the trees on its banks. He soon saw that the lake had been made by beavers. He took his station at a certain spot to see whether any of the beavers would show themselves. Soon he saw the head of one peeping out of the water to see who the stranger was.

'My friend,' said Pauppukkeewis, 'could you not turn me into a bear like yourself?'

'I do not know,' replied the beaver; 'I will go and ask the others.'

Soon all the beavers showed their heads above the water, and looked to see if Pauppukkeewis was armed, but he had left his bow and arrows in a hollow tree a short distance off. When they were satisfied they all came near.

'Can you not, with all your united power,' said he, 'turn me into a beaver? I wish to live among you.'

'Yes,' answered the chief, 'lie down;' and Pauppukkeewis soon found himself changed into one of them.

'You must make me large,' said he, 'larger than any of you.'

'Yes, yes,' said they; 'by and by, when we get into the lodge, it shall be done.'

They all dived into the lake, and Pauppukkeewis passing large heaps of limbs of trees and logs at the bottom, asked the use of them. The beavers answered:

'They are our winter provisions.'

When they all got into the lodge their number was about 100. The lodge was large and warm.

'Now we will make you large,' said they, exerting all their power. 'Will that do?'

'Yes,' he answered, for he found he was ten times the size of the largest.

'You need not go out,' said they. 'We will bring your food into the lodge, and you shall be our chief.'

'Very well,' answered Pauppukkeewis. He thought:

'I will stay here and grow fat at their expense.' But very soon a beaver came into the lodge out of breath, crying:

'We are attacked by Indians.'

All huddled together in great fear. The water began to lower, for the hunters had broken down the dam, and soon the beavers heard them on the roof of the lodge, breaking it in. Out jumped all the beavers and so escaped. Pauppukkeewis tried to follow them, but, alas! They had made him so large that he could not creep out of the hole. He called to them to come back, but none answered. He worried himself so much in trying to escape that he looked like a bladder. He could not change himself into a man again though he heard and understood all the hunters said. One of them put his head in at the top of the lodge.

'Ty-au!' cried he. 'Tut-ty-au! Me-shau-mik! King of the beavers is in.'

Then they all got at Pauppukkeewis and battered in his skull with their clubs. After that seven or eight of them placed his body on poles and carried him home. As he went he reflected:

'What will become of me? My ghost or shadow will not die after they get me to their lodges.'

When the party arrived home, they sent out invitations to a grand feast. The women took Pauppukkeewis and laid him in the snow to skin him, but as soon as his flesh got cold, his jee-bi, or spirit, fled.

Pauppukkeewis found himself standing on a prairie, having assumed his mortal shape. After walking a short distance, he saw a herd of elks feeding. He admired the apparent ease and enjoyment of their life, and thought there could be nothing more pleasant than to have the liberty of running about, and feeding on the prairies. He asked them if they could not change him into an elk.

'Yes,' they answered, after a pause. 'Get down on your hands and feet.' He did so, and soon found himself an elk.

'I want big horns and big feet,' said he. 'I wish to be very large.'

'Yes, yes,' they said. 'There,' exerting all their power, 'are you big enough?'

'Yes,' he answered, for he saw he was very large.

They spent a good time in playing and running.

Being rather cold one day he went into a thick wood for shelter, and was followed by most of the herd. They had not been there long before some elks from behind passed them like a strong wind. All took the alarm, and off they ran, Pauppukkeewis with the rest.

'Keep out on the plains,' said they, but he found it was too late to do so, for they had already got entangled in the thick woods. He soon smelt the hunters, who were closely following his trail, for they had left all the others to follow him. He jumped furiously, and broke down young trees in his flight, but it only served to retard his progress. He soon felt an arrow in his side. He jumped over trees in his agony, but the arrows clattered thicker and thicker about him, and at last one entered his heart. He fell to the ground and heard the whoop of triumph given by the warriors. On coming up they looked at the carcass with astonishment, and with their hands up to their mouths, exclaimed:

'Ty-au! ty-au!'

There were about 60 in the party, who had come out on a special hunt, for one of their number had, the day before, observed Pauppukkeewis's large tracks in the sand. They skinned him, and as his flesh got cold his jee-bi took its flight, and once more he found himself in human shape.

His passion for adventure was not yet cooled. On coming to a large lake, the shore of which was sandy, he saw a large flock of brant, and, speaking to them, he asked them to turn him into a brant.

'Very well,' said they.

'But I want to be very large,' said he.

'Very well,' replied the brant, and he soon found himself one of them, of prodigious size, all the others looking on at him in amazement.

'You must fly as leader,' they said.

'No,' replied Pauppukkeewis, 'I will fly behind.'

'Very well,' said they. 'One thing we have to say to you. You must be careful in flying not to look down, for if you do something may happen to you.'

'Be it so,' said he, and soon the flock rose up in the air, for they were bound for the north. They flew very fast with Pauppukkeewis behind. One day, while going with a strong wind, and as swift as their wings would flap, while they passed over a large village, the Indians below raised a great shout, for they were amazed at the enormous size of Pauppukkeewis. They made such a noise that Pauppukkeewis forgot what had been told him about not looking down. He was flying as swift as an arrow, and as soon as he brought his neck in, and stretched it down to look at the shouters, his tail was caught by the wind, and he was blown over and over. He tried to right himself, but without success. Down he went from an immense height, turning over and over. He lost his senses, and when he recovered them he found himself jammed in a cleft in a hollow tree. To get backward or forward was impossible, and there he remained until his brant life was ended by starvation. Then his jee-bi again left the carcass, and once more he found himself in human shape.

Travelling was still his passion, and one day he came to a lodge, in which were two old men whose heads were white from age. They treated him well, and he told them he was going back to his village to see his friends and people. The old men said they would aid him, and pointed out the way they said he should go, but they were deceivers. After walking all day he came to a lodge very like the first, and looking in he found two old men with white heads. It was in fact the very same lodge, and he had been walking in a circle. The old men did not undeceive him, but pretended to be strangers, and said in a kind voice:

'We will show you the way.'

After walking the third day, and coming back to the same place, he discovered their trickery, for he had cut a notch in the door-post.

'Who are you,' said he to them, 'to treat *me* so?' and he gave one a kick and the other a slap that killed them. Their blood flew against the rocks near their lodge, and that is the reason there are red streaks in them to this day. Then Pauppukkeewis burned their lodge.

He continued his journey, not knowing exactly which way to go. At last he came to a big lake. He ascended the highest hill to try and see the opposite shore, but he could not, so he made a canoe and took a sail on the water. On looking down he saw that the bottom of the lake was covered with dark fish, of which he caught some. This made him wish to return to his village, and bring his people to live near this lake. He sailed on, and towards evening came to an island, where he stopped and ate the fish.

Next day he returned to the mainland, and, while wandering along the shore, he encountered a more powerful manito than himself, named Manabozho. Pauppukkeewis thought it best, after playing him a trick, to keep out of his way. He again thought of returning to his village, and, transforming himself into a partridge, took his flight towards it. In a short time he reached it, and his return was welcomed with feasting and songs. He told them of the lake and of the fish, and, telling them that it would be easier for them to live there, persuaded them all to remove. He immediately began to lead them by short journeys, and all things turned out as he had said.

While the people lived there a messenger came to Pauppukkeewis in the shape of a bear, and said that the bear-chief wished to see him at once at his village. Pauppukkeewis was ready in an instant, and getting on the messenger's back was carried away. Towards evening they ascended a high mountain, and came to a cave, in which the bear-chief lived. He was a very large creature, and he made Pauppukkeewis welcome, inviting him into his lodge.

As soon as propriety allowed he spoke, and said that he had sent for him because he had heard he was the chief who was leading a large party towards his hunting-grounds.

'You must know,' said he, 'that you have no right there, and I wish you to leave the country with your party, or else we must fight.'

'Very well,' replied Pauppukkeewis, 'so be it.'

He did not wish to do anything without consulting his people, and he saw that the bear-chief was raising a war-party, so he said he would go back that night. The bear-king told him he might do as he wished, and that one of the bears was at his command; so Pauppukkeewis, jumping on its back, rode home. Then he assembled the village, and told the young men to kill the bear, make ready a feast, and hang the head outside the village, for he knew the bear spies would soon see it and carry the news to their chief.

Next morning Pauppukkeewis got all his young warriors ready for the fight. After waiting one day, the bear war-party came in sight, making a tremendous noise. The bear-chief advanced, and said that he did not wish to shed the blood of the young warriors, but if Pauppukkeewis would consent they two would run a race, and the winner should kill the losing chief, and all the loser's followers should be the slaves of the other. Pauppukkeewis agreed, and they ran before all the warriors. He was victor; but not to terminate the race too quickly he gave the bear-chief some specimens of his skill, forming eddies and whirlwinds with the sand as he twisted and turned about. As the bear-chief came to the post Pauppukkeewis drove an arrow through him. Having done this he told his young men to take the bears and tie one at the door of each lodge, that they might remain in future as slaves.

After seeing that all was quiet and prosperous in the village, Pauppukkeewis felt his desire for adventure returning, so he took an affectionate leave of his friends and people, and started off again. After wandering a long time, he came to the lodge of Manabozho, who was absent. Pauppukkeewis thought he would play him a trick, so he turned everything in the lodge upside down and killed his chickens. Now Manabozho calls all the fowl of the air his chickens, and among the number was a raven, the meanest of birds, and him Pauppukkeewis killed and hung up by the neck to insult Manabozho. He then went on till he came to a very high point of rocks running out into the lake, from the top of which he could see the country as far as the eye could reach. While he sat there, Manabozho's mountain chickens flew round and past him in great numbers. So, out of spite, he shot many of them, for his arrows were sure and the birds many, and he amused himself by throwing the birds down the precipice. At length a wary bird called out:

'Pauppukkeewis is killing us: go and tell our father.'

Away flew some of them, and Manabozho soon made his appearance on the plain below.

Pauppukkeewis slipped down the other side of the mountain. Manabozho cried from the top:

'The earth is not so large but I can get up to you.'

Off Pauppukkeewis ran and Manabozho after him. He ran over hills and prairies with all his speed, but his pursuer was still hard after him. Then he thought of a shift. He stopped, and climbed a large pine-tree, stripped it of all its green foliage, and threw it to the winds. Then he ran on. When Manabozho reached the tree, it called out to him:

'Great Manabozho, give me my life again. Pauppukkeewis has killed me.'

'I will do so,' said Manabozho, and it took him some time to gather the scattered foliage. Then he resumed the chase. Pauppukkeewis repeated the same trick with the hemlock, and with other trees, for Manabozho would always stop to restore anything that called upon him to give it life again. By this means Pauppukkeewis kept ahead, but still Manabozho was overtaking him when Pauppukkeewis saw an elk. He asked it to take him on its back, and this the animal did, and for a time he made great progress. Still Manabozho was in sight. Pauppukkeewis dismounted, and, coming to a large sandstone rock, he broke it in pieces, and scattered the grains. Manabozho was so close upon him at this place that he had almost caught him, but the foundation of the rock cried out:

'Haye! Ne-me-sho! Pauppukkeewis has spoiled me. Will you not restore me to life?'

'Yes,' replied Manabozho, and he restored the rock to its previous shape. He then pushed on in pursuit of Pauppukkeewis, and had got so near as to put out his arm to seize him, when Pauppukkeewis dodged him, and raised such a dust and commotion by whirlwinds, as to make the trees break and the sand and leaves dance in the air. Again and again Manabozho's hand was put out to catch him, but he dodged him at every turn, and at last, making a great dust, he dashed into a hollow tree, which had been blown down, and, changing himself into a snake, crept out at its roots. Well that he did; for at the moment Manabozho, who is Ogee-bau-ge-mon (a species of lightning) struck the tree with all his power, and shivered it to fragments. Pauppukkeewis again took human shape, and again Manabozho, pursuing him, pressed him hard.

At a distance Pauppukkeewis saw a very high rock jutting out into a lake, and he ran for the foot of the precipice, which was abrupt and elevated. As he came near, the manito of the rock opened his door and told him to come in. No sooner was the door closed than Manabozho knocked at it.

'Open,' he cried in a loud voice.

The manito was afraid of him, but said to his guest:

'Since I have sheltered you, I would sooner die with you than open the door.'

'Open,' Manabozho cried again.

The manito was silent. Manabozho made no attempt to force the door open. He waited a few moments.

'Very well,' said he, 'I give you till night to live.'

The manito trembled, for he knew that when the hour came he would be shut up under the earth.

Night came, the clouds hung low and black, and every moment the forked lightning flashed from them. The black clouds advanced slowly and threw their dark shadows afar, and behind was heard the rumbling noise of the coming thunder. When the clouds were gathered over the rock the thunder roared, the lightning flashed, the ground shook, and the solid rock split, tottered, and fell. Under the ruins lay crushed the mortal bodies of Pauppukkeewis and the manito.

It was only then that Pauppukkeewis found that he was really dead. He had been killed before in the shapes of different animals, but now his body, in human shape, was crushed.

Manabozho came and took his jee-bi, or spirit. 'You,' said he to Pauppukkeewis, 'shall not be again permitted to live on the earth. I will give you the shape of the war-eagle, and you shall be the chief of all birds, and your duty shall be to watch over their destinies.'

BATTLE OF THE OWLS

(HAWAIIAN)

There lived a man named Kapoi, at Kahehuna, in Honolulu, who went one day to Kewalo to get some thatching for his house. On his way back he found some owl's eggs, which he gathered together and brought home with him. In the evening he wrapped them in ti leaves and was about to roast them in hot ashes, when an owl perched on the fence which surrounded his house and called out to him, 'O Kapoi, give me my eggs!'

Kapoi asked the owl, 'How many eggs had you?'

'Seven eggs,' replied the owl.

Kapoi then said, 'Well, I wish to roast these eggs for my supper.'

The owl asked the second time for its eggs, and was answered by Kapoi in the same manner. Then said the owl, 'O heartless Kapoi! why don't you take pity on me? Give me my eggs.'

Kapoi then told the owl to come and take them.

The owl, having got the eggs, told Kapoi to build up a *heiau*, or temple, and instructed him to make an altar and call the temple by the name of Manua. Kapoi built the temple as directed; set kapu days for its dedication, and placed the customary sacrifice on the altar.

News spread to the hearing of Kakuihewa, who was then King of Oahu, living at the time at Waikiki, that a certain man had kapued certain days for his heiau, and had already dedicated it. This King had made a law that whoever among his people should erect a heiau and kapu the same before the King had his temple kapued, that man should pay the penalty of death. Kapoi was thereupon seized, by the King's orders, and led to the heiau of Kupalaha, at Waikiki.

That same day, the owl that had told Kapoi to erect a temple gathered all the owls from Lanai, Maui, Molokai, and Hawaii to one place at Kalapueo. All those from the Koolau districts were assembled at Kanoniakapueo, and those from Kauai and Niihau at Pueohulunui, near Moanalua.

It was decided by the King that Kapoi should be put to death on the day of Kane. When that day came, at daybreak the owls left their places of rendezvous and covered the whole sky over Honolulu; and as the King's servants seized Kapoi to put him to death, the owls flew at them, pecking them with their beaks and scratching them with their claws. Then and there was fought the battle between Kakuihewa's people and the owls. At last the owls conquered, and Kapoi was released, the King acknowledging that his *Akua* (god) was a powerful one. From that time the owl has been recognized as one of the many deities venerated by the Hawaiian people.